INTRODUCTION TO PALEOECOLOGY

Original title by R. F. Gekker

VVEDENIYE V. PALEOEKOLOGIYU

Moscow, 1957

INTRODUCTION TO PALEOECOLOGY

By

R. F. HECKER

The spelling of the author's name on this page as R. F. Hecker is the westernized spelling preferred by the author. On the other hand, the Foreword and Bibliography show his name as R. F. Gekker, which is the spelling found in various Russian publications.

Translated from the Russian,
edited, and prepared for publication by
Professor M. K. Elias and Professor R. C. Moore,
in cooperation with Scripta Technica.
The translation was sponsored by the
American Geological Institute
and supported by the
National Science Foundation.

AMERICAN ELSEVIER PUBLISHING COMPANY, INC.
NEW YORK
1965

SOLE DISTRIBUTORS FOR GREAT BRITAIN
ELSEVIER PUBLISHING COMPANY, LTD.
Barking, Essex, England

SOLE DISTRIBUTORS FOR THE CONTINENT OF EUROPE
ELSEVIER PUBLISHING COMPANY
Amsterdam, The Netherlands

Library of Congress Catalog Card Number: 65-16708

Contents

Foreword

Paleoecology* is a part of paleontology. It is concerned with the relationship between organisms of the geologic past and their life medium, much as ecology (neoecology) is concerned with the same problem in respect to living organisms. Setting up and solving paleoecological problems has considerable economic, as well as academic, importance. These possibly may be solved only with help from the adjacent sciences, mainly biological and geological—using methods developed by these sciences, as well as its own paleoecologic methods.

Paleoecology is of prime importance for theoretical biology, and, therefore, for the theory of evolution. This is so because the problem of organic evolution is, to a considerable extent, an ecological problem—or, more precisely, a paleoecological one. At the base of the evolutionary problem is clarification of the process of the origin of species under impact of external and internal factors. Understanding of actions by external factors upon ancient organisms is one of the paleoecological problems.

When studying ecologically the remains of extinct organisms and the sediments in which they are embedded, it becomes possible to evaluate adaptation of the organisms to the conditions of their life: to follow up their development (evolution) in connection with these conditions and their changes in the course of time, and thus to find a way toward elucidation of the causes and conditions which control morphogenesis.

The problem of organic evolution is the most complex and difficult among biological problems, and paleoecologist-paleontologists should take part in its solution.

Everyday work by a systematic paleontologist, so important for differentiation and correlation of sedimentary

*From paleo- (Gr., palaios) = ancient; eco (Gr., oikos) = house, dwellings; -logy (Gr., logos) = knowledge, science.

deposits, does not attain its full significance unless it takes into account general ecological laws and the particular ecology of the organisms with which it is concerned. It is a matter of fact that sound systematic classification of an organism (generic, specific, and so on) requires not only knowledge of its morphological peculiarities, its ontogeny and phylogeny, but also of its functional morphology, its ecology, and its biogeography.

Taxonomy of fossil organisms, when it does not take into account their relationship to inorganic and organic surroundings, frequently becomes artificial and rigidly formal, not reflecting actual blood relationships between various forms. Neglect of ecological data may result in incorrect arrangement of phylogenetic lineages and, through this, in erroneous understanding of evolutionary processes. Forms which actually are not closely related, but which merely existed under similar conditions and therefore developed convergently, may be erroneously placed in the same genetic lineage. On the other hand, some forms may be classed arbitrarily far apart from each other on the evidence of some features which seem important to a systematist, but which actually could have varied easily under the impact of changing life conditions. Such errors can be avoided through elucidation of the adaptive significance of this or that characteristic.

Cognizance of all general data on ecology and geography of various species is also necessary for proper stratigraphic utilization of fossil organisms. Many examples are known where neglect of basic ecological principles has led to synchronization of heterochronous homofacial faunas on the basis of similarity of form and their association owing to similarity of life conditions, whereas some actually synchronous faunas, which lived under different conditions (heterofacial faunas) and which accordingly lack common forms, have been erroneously assigned to different ages.

Such errors are easily revealed and eliminated when an ecological approach to the study of fossil organisms is adopted. Likewise, paleoecological data help a biostratigrapher to achieve a more detailed differention of sedimentary sequences than is possible without them.

Paleoecological analysis of faunas and floras permits an understanding of their remains not only as representatives of systematic groups and as geologic time indicators, but also as participants in the creation of a definite medium, as indicators of facies situations and conditions in which particular sediments were deposited. Mere lithologic study of ancient sediments does not always provide sufficient evidence for understanding their genesis. In such cases an ecologic analysis of the faunas and floras may elucidate the conditions under which sedimentary deposition took place. Moreover, even more than the rocks themselves, fossil organisms are frequently exact indicators of a habitat medium, and of a medium in which the sediments accumulated. The data obtained by ecologic analysis may be utilized for elucidation of the genesis of sedimentary mineral deposits. Knowledge of their genesis is certainly essential for proper direction of exploration, prospecting, and exploitation. Paleoecological analysis is of the greatest importance in construction of detailed paleogeographic, as well as paleoclimatic, interpretations. It may also render substantial assistance in deciphering regional tectonic processes.

Introduction of a paleoecological approach in paleontological lectures enlivens discussions of fossil materials and elucidates the significance of morphological peculiarities in fossil organisms.

The enormous territory of the Soviet Union contains various sediments which represent all geologic ages and facies (e.g., platforms, geosynclines, foothill and intermountain troughs); here lie complete ancient basins, seas of various depths, and also land masses of varying geologic antiquity, with their water basins located in different climatic belts; sediments in many instances are only slightly altered.

All this presents inexhaustible material for paleoecological investigations. Thus we are confronted with an enormous, almost unembraceable field of activity, with most interesting materials and most alluring perspectives for research.

Scarceness of paleoecological compendia or instructions for paleoecological research in the world geological literature,* and the accumulated personal experience

*In 1940, the Division of Geology and Geography, National Research Council, U.S.A., created a Subcommittee on the Ecology of Marine Organisms. This subcommittee, in 1942, became a Committee on Marine Ecology as related to

gained in the course of paleoecological investigations of
the biota in the Main Devonian Field of the Russian Platform, prompted me to prepare an article entitled "Principles and Instruction for Paleoecological Investigations"
(R. F. Gekker, 1933). Two revised editions of the paper
were published in 1954 and 1955 under the title "Instruction for Paleoecological Investigations" (R. F. Gekker,
1954b, 1955).

The present *Introduction to Paleoecology* is an enlarged
version of the two latter publications. In writing it I have
utilized the latest experience and the data accumulated in
the course of 25 years of studying faunas and floras of
ancient marine and nonmarine water basins, this work
having been conducted by me and my associates in the Paleoecological Laboratory, Paleontological Institute, Academy of Sciences of the U.S.S.R. The data from national
and international literature published in the course of these
years have also been utilized. The cited discussions of
1933, 1954 and 1955, as well as the present *Introduction,*
are designed for the use of specialists in paleontology and
geology, and for students of these disciplines. They will
serve to acquaint them with the problems and methods of
paleoecological investigations.

I trust that the *Introduction* will be of help in geological
studies by groups of specialists and other geological and
paleontological investigations, and will contribute toward
improvement in the training of young paleontologists and
geologists. I also hope that it will inform ecologists among
zoologists and botanists about problems confronted by
paleoecologists, and about the methods they use in efforts
to solve them. This may promote the organization of joint
investigations by neontologists and paleontologists.

Paleontology and, in 1957, issued an authoritative multiauthor book in two
volumes, "Treatise on Marine Ecology and Paleoecology." In 1963, D.V. Ager
published his standard work, "Principles of Paleoecology" and, in 1964, the
book "Approaches to Paleoecology" (Wiley, New York) appeared under the
editorship of J. Imbrie and N. Newell.

CHAPTER I

History, Objectives and Methods of Paleoecology

1. HISTORY OF PALEOECOLOGY

The oldest written record of observations in the field of what we now call paleoecology are found with the ancient Greeks (Xenophanes of Colophon, circa 500 B.C.). Nineteen centuries later, Leonardo da Vinci speculated about the conditions under which fossil shells had been buried. However, it was not until the 18th and 19th centuries that paleoecological studies really began. Among the founders of this field of research, the Italian L. F. Marsigli (1658-1730), the Frenchman H. Milne Edwards (1800-1885) and the Englishman E. Forbes (1815-1854) should especially be mentioned. In Russia, it was Vladimir Onufrievich Kovalevskiy (1842-1883) who initiated fundamental paleoecological analysis of fossil organisms. His work, chiefly on terrestrial Tertiary mammals, provides brilliant examples of evolutionary, functional, and paleoecological study of fossil organisms. He has shown how dry, purely descriptive paleontology can be replaced by a truly scientific paleontology, which "vitalizes" the petrified remains of ancient organisms as it reveals their connection with and dependence on surrounding media, and demonstrates the adaptive significance of their morphological structures. Paleontology thus becomes a science of organic evolution, built upon a concrete and profound understanding of paleontological materials.

Kovalevskiy did not propose any special term for the new ecological direction in paleontology undertaken by him. It was later on that the designation *ethologopaleontological** study was proposed by one of his successors—the

---

* From etho-(Gr., ethos) = custom, habit.

Belgian paleontologist L. Dollo (1909)—and that of *paleo-biological* study by another—the Austrian paleontologist O. Abel (1912). At present this type of investigation is called *paleoecological*, and we speak of paleoecology as a major division of paleontology. It is entitled to as much independence as animal ecology and plant ecology are given within the frames of zoology and botany. Thus, paleoecologists came to be distinguished among paleontologists as specialists working particularly on problems of the ecology of fossil organisms.

Kovalevskiy was not the first among Russian paleontologists to consider the dependence of ancient organisms on the conditions in which they lived. Even in the pre-Darwinian era, before Kovalevskiy, a professor at Moscow University, zoologist and paleontologist K. F. Rouillier (1814-1858), conceived the idea of intimate relationships between Jurassic marine invertebrates and the conditions of their life.

Subsequent to Kovalevskiy's classical investigations on the evolution of ancient organisms, an ecological analysis of fossil forms was made by N. I. Andrusov (1861-1924). The materials on which he worked were Tertiary and Quaternary mollusks from marine and brackish-water basins of southern European Russia. He interpreted development of the molluscan faunas and the morphogenesis of different ecological types as intimately connected with changes in the character of the basins. On this concrete base a detailed stratigraphic scheme of the Neogene and Quaternary deposits of the southern part of the U.S.S.R. was created—a scheme which has not lost value even in our time. At a later date he carried his paleoecological investigations into a unique fossil fauna, that of the Kerch and Taman bryozoan reefs. A few other Russian paleontologists followed the path blazed by Kovalevskiy and Andrusov. Such was the work by A. P. Karpinsky (1847-1936) on specialized Permian fishes (edestids) and Devonian trochiliscids (related to the modern alga *Chara*); he utilized all available data, including the conditions of their occurrence and characters of the enclosing rocks. At the beginning of this century, N. N. Yakovlev started to publish his investigations on tetracorals and brachiopods, and later on crinoids. In these works he viewed their morphogenesis in the light of their life conditions.

Interrelationships between organisms and their environment were considered in the classical works by A. D. Arkhangelskiy (1879-1940) and M. E. Noinskiy (1875-1932).

The works of Karpinskiy and Yakovlev were dedicated primarily to selected genera and species, those of Kovalevskiy and Andrusov to groups of related genera and species, and studies by Noinskiy and Arkhangelskiy to whole faunas. In some of these works the mode of life and the life conditions of extinct organisms were considered, and also their influence upon the development of new morphological characteristics (Kovalevskiy, Yakovlev, Andrusov). In other works no such analysis was undertaken, since the authors visualized overall conditions of life and the fate of whole faunas as controlled by conditions of their existence, and observed changes in these conditions (Noinskiy). In some investigations the rocks in which the fossils have been enclosed were studied (Arkhangelskiy, Karpinskiy, Noinskiy); no such investigation was conducted in others (Kovalevskiy, Yakovlev). Thus, all these works were conducted in paleoecological direction but their contents are different, and their authors have utilized only parts of the research possibilities which are offered to a paleoecologist-paleontologist by the fossil material.

It is also necessary to point out that in a majority of these works principal attention was directed to a morphogenetic and functional analysis of the fossilized organic forms, whereas the biotic medium (complex of organic forms) in which the organisms lived and their physical life conditions were not adequately studied; yet knowledge of these aspects of life is necessary for a more profound understanding of the ancient organic world. For a proper reconstruction of life conditions we need detailed and properly directed lithologic investigations, and must also utilize a number of other geological data. With the exception of papers by Arkhangelskiy and Noinskiy, no such efforts were made by the other investigators mentioned.

The organization of broadly conceived paleoecological investigations in the U.S.S.R. became possible after the organization in 1930 by A.A. Borisyak (1872-1944) of the Paleozoological (later named Paleontological) Institute of the Academy of Sciences of the U.S.S.R. In this institute a paleoecological laboratory was created with the aim of organizing paleoecological investigations of varying scope and scale (mostly large), and the working out of methods for such investigations.

2. PALEOECOLOGY AND BIOLOGICAL PROBLEMS

The foremost problems for a paleoecologist are:

1) Elucidation of the *mode of life* of extinct animals and plants, so as to a) understand these organisms more completely and profoundly, and b) determine the influence they may have exercised upon other animals and plants, and upon their inorganic medium of life.

2) Reconstruction of the *life conditions* of various organisms, taken both separately and in association during the geological past, so as to determine the possibilities which then existed for their development as individuals and as associations.

Life habits (feeding, locomotion, aggression and defense, peculiarities of propagation, care of offspring, seasonal and other phenomena) and life conditions controlled both by abiotic media (bottom character of concern to bottom-dwellers, salinity, temperature, degree of water agitation, gaseous regime, etc.) and by biotic media (food, competitors, enemies, parasites, peaceful cohabitants, and others) are fundamental elements on which should be based an understanding of the interrelations between organisms, as well as between them and inorganic factors of habitats. Fossilized organic remains, rocks which enclose them and in which peculiarities of their habitat are imprinted, as well as distribution of all these elements in geological sections of the earth, comprise the material for works directed toward solution of paleoecological problems.

Modes of life and conditions of organic habitation are interdependent. When conducting paleoecological investigations it is necessary to pursue answers to both of these problems.

In order to judge the mode of life of extinct organisms it is necessary to analyze structures which reflect their activities; additional knowledge of their life medium only supplements the conclusions of such morphofunctional analysis. Conditions of the habitat of ancient organisms are also elucidated by their structure, but not sufficiently. In order to ascertain details of their mode of life, it is necessary to analyze their habitat by study of the rock in which organisms are preserved and investigation of the indirect signs which environment impressed upon them. Here is an example: the presence in a pelecypod shell of a gap in the anterior and posterior ends, and possession of desmodont dentition, indicate that it belongs among burrowing forms. This deduction occasionally can be directly verified by finding the shell in its vertical life position. However, a more complete conclusion as to life habitat of these mollusks, including character of the bottom and its depth, salinity and gas content of the water, biotic factors, etc., can be achieved only through study of the composition of the rock which encloses the shells, its texture and bedding-surface peculiarities, and vertical and lateral changes in the surrounding sedimentary rocks, as well as by study of the assemblages of accompanying organic forms, and their changes in space and time.

Paleontologists face an enormous task in elucidating the ecology of fossil organisms known as yet only by general descriptions and names (such is the majority of fossils), and also in explaining the adaptive and functional significance of their morphological peculiarities (morpho-ecological and morphofunctional analysis).

In an ecological approach to fossil organisms it is necessary fully to evaluate the dependence of their morphology on conditions of their habitat, and on changes in these conditions. When using this approach a different, more nearly correct evaluation is given to this or that morphological peculiarity in fossil forms, and different criteria will appear to be most important in differentiation of various systematic categories: genera, species, subspecies, varieties. It will become understood also that it is unthinkable to differentiate species by differences in size for very large, or, on the other hand, for very small specimens,* because these forms may represent individuals of one and the same species, and represent very

---

*However, when a steady increase in size of apparently the same species is observed in the course of geologic time (Elias, Newell), it is proper to differentiate each established phyletic stage by an informal sign, usually greek letters: α, β, γ, and so on, thus indicating successive time "mutations" (of Waagen, not de Vries), now termed waagenons (Caster, Elias), the increasing size being accompanied by no obvious morphological changes that would justify differentiation into subspecies or even genera.—Tr.

different stages of ontogeny; or on the evidence of casual deviation from a norm, induced in the course of life (e.g., shell distortion because of density of living conditions, or because of individual conditions of attachment to substrata, etc.).

Furthermore, in an ecological approach paleontologists do not consider their work completed after a mere distribution of materials among known and new species (or other systematic categories), as is usually done in most paleontological investigations; rather they attempt to elucidate the process of evolution, to conceive the initiation of this or that genus, species, or smaller systematic category.

Besides the problems concerning mode of existence, life conditions and facies occurrence of separate forms, groups of related forms, biocoenoses, etc., a paleoecologist must set before himself other paleoecological as well as general paleontological problems, the elucidation of which demands participation of a paleoecologist. Examples are: a) the concrete interrelationship between various organisms and peculiarities of their cohabitation; b) boundaries of areal distribution of each form; c) density or rarefaction of communities, and possibility of overpopulation in some particular districts; d) struggle for survival, natural selection and its creative role; e) variability of forms and its dependence on an external medium; f) elimination of some forms by adverse changes in the medium, and survival of others coupled with changes in them; g) dependence of the origin of species on the external medium and on its changes; h) rates of origin of species, and their relationship to the tempo of changes in the medium; i) directed morphogenesis in various phyletic lineages, and changes of evolutionary direction in them in connection with changes in life conditions; j) structural convergence in organisms which lived in similar ecological conditions, and correlative changes in these organisms; k) migration of organisms, its causes, tempo, and consequences, etc.

Working out of the enumerated problems is apt to lead an investigator to establishment of *special and general principles pertaining to the development of the organic world.*

The facts concerning sequences of faunas and floras and of separate systematic groups and forms in the course of geologic time are well known. However, such succession in time (that is, elucidation of evolution) is usually connected with evolution of the life medium (abiotic and biotic) only in a very general way. The working out of these problems can be substantially deepened and expanded if an organism is considered always in conjunction with other organisms and with the abiotic medium.

Such investigations will show not only a succession in time and evolution of various groups of organisms, but they will also disclose the *evolution of biocoenoses*, that is, a change during geologic time of interconnected forms that lived in similar environments. Also, they will show gradual replacement of more ancient forms with lower organization by more highly organized forms. In this way the successions of various classes, genera, and species belonging to different systematic groups and "vicarious in time" may be traced. They have been adapted to similar life conditions, and accordingly produce similar "life forms" with convergent characteristics (see p. 11). The origin of various adaptive characteristics within groups of fossil organisms, and each of them taken separately, will be elucidated, and changes in these adaptive characteristics in the course of geological history will be established.

These problems pertain to the process of developing ecological interrelationships between various organisms, and between them and the abiotic medium. This process has been termed *ecogenesis* (Davitashvili, 1947, 1948).

3. GENERAL METHODS OF INVESTIGATION

In addition to morphofunctional analysis of the preserved remains of fossil forms, paleoecological analysis may proceed, generally speaking, in three principal directions: *1*) comparative analysis of forms per se and of their systematic groups and biocoenoses, composed of different but contemporaneous fossil facies; *2*) comparative analysis of forms per se and of their systematic groups and biocoenoses, composed of the same but heterochronous fossile facies; *3*) comparative analysis of the ecology of a particular group (possibly also of a biocoenosis and of a form per se with changing of its life in the course of geological time.

For the purpose of comparative analysis, it follows that one must compare the biocoenoses and the forms per se which *differ in age and in conditions of their life*, because a paleoecological study of paleontological material from only one locality, or only one bed, is insufficient.

The *method of the widest possible comparative analysis* of the faunas, floras, biocoenoses, thanatocoenoses, and sediments in which they are enclosed is especially fruitful in the work of a paleoecologist. This comparison should include our epoch.

Different groups of forms and different biocoenoses demand different comparative material for their elucidation. The larger a body of observations, for instance, the larger must be the number of comparable sedimentary cross sections of a particular ancient basin and the more definite and interesting are the resultant conclusions. For example, in the course of paleoecological investigations in Fergana about 50 sections of Paleogene deposits along the periphery of the Fergana depression were studied, as well as the faunas and the lithology of all Paleogene stages (R. F. Gekker et al., 1963). This organization of the work produced a vast amount of comparative material, which made possible a number of well-substantiated conclusions concerning life conditions in the different parts of the Fergana Bay of the Paleogene sea. These conditions, which changed greatly during Paleogene times, controlled development of the local fauna and flora. Such conclusions would not be possible from study of only a few sections, particularly if these were confined to a certain part of the Fergana depression, or if they were restricted to stages and horizons of the Paleogene which contain the most prolific fauna.

The basic method of an ecologist (neoecologist) in the study of the world of living organisms is observation of the organisms in their natural environment. Besides this a neoecologist can organize experiments, whereas a paleoecologist cannot do so. However, the whole geological history of the organic world may be regarded as an uninterrupted series of "experiments by nature" affecting the inhabitants of ancient seas and lands, forcing them to shift location with migrating facies and to adapt themselves to new conditions, and thus to undergo change or else perish. These "experiments by nature" are incomparably grander than those which man can possibly organize. What we can do, however, is to elucidate the conditions under which such "experiments" have taken place, and thus come closer to understanding the causes behind the changes that happened in the plant and animal worlds.

The methods in a paleoecologist's work are therefore, in this respect, opposite those used by neoecologists. A neoecologist creates experimental conditions in order to obtain results quite unknown to him in advance, whereas a paleoecologist must undertake to reconstruct the conditions and causes of changes indicated by the preserved fossil material resulting from "experiments by nature."*

4. ACTUALISTIC METHODS

Considerable help in solving paleoecological problems is derived from actualistic methods. The great significance of these methods for paleontology, not only in former, narrower practice, when living organisms were utilized for better understanding of their fossil relatives, was properly appraised by R. Richter (1928b), who distinguished a special study in paleontology—*actuopaleontology*—the purpose of which is to learn about the conditions that lead now to the producing of fossil "documents" and that accordingly may be inferred by a paleontologist in interpreting the conditions associated with making fossils in the geological past. The first step in working out a program of actuopaleontologic investigation was the establishment of a special marine station, at which very carefully planned observations could be conducted of modern organisms and, particularly, of mechanisms which control the manner of burial of organic remains in the littoral and shallow-water belt in the North Sea. Simultaneously studies were

---

*Although an experiment, in its usual meaning, cannot possibly be organized by a paleoecologist, he is nevertheless in a position to experiment in certain ways with fossil skeletal remains. Some examples of this are found in the literature. Thus experiments have been conducted for the purpose of determining calyx orientation in respect to current direction of living individuals of the Devonian coral *Calceola* (Richter, 1929b), and also for elucidating the life orientation of fossil oysters possessing massive convex shells and post-mortem orientation of concavo-convex oyster valves.

organized on the conditions of marine sedimentation which could elucidate the origin of the same kind of sediments in the geological past—*actuogeological investigations*, according to Richter.

Although the possibilities for such work are much greater in the U.S.S.R., they have been utilized almost not at all by Soviet paleontologists. U.S.S.R. territory is bordered by 11 seas, on the shores of some of which are marine biological stations: at Murmansk on the Barents Sea, at Sevastopol and Karadag on the Black Sea, one on Lake Baikal, and others. A whole fleet of exploration craft includes the ship "Vityaz' " which has quite up-to-date technical equipment for oceanographic investigations.

The study of living animals and plants from an ecological point of view should be combined with elaborate investigation of the substratum which they inhabit and of other factors of the medium, as well as with study of the processes of disintegration of organic remains, and peculiarities of their burial. Such investigations by a paleoecologist will benefit not only his own discipline, but by his observations and generalizations will enrich the sciences of living organisms. The point is that a paleontologist is interested in many things, for instance in the tracks left by animals on the sea bottom, in animal excrements, etc., to which zoologists, working on these same organisms, pay insufficient attention. However, when using actualistic methods we should never utilize the results of observations on living organisms *directly* on the related fossil forms, because life conditions of the former and latter could in some way differ, and the same can be said concerning their life habits. It should be pointed out, incidentally, that the ecology of living organisms has as yet been studied very incompletely, and accumulated data frequently have not been integrated. Because of this, a paleoecologist who wishes to utilize ecological data on living forms is compelled at the outset to make some preliminary generalizations based on data in the widely scattered literature.

Through acquaintance with the literature on living forms, and also by making his own observations on them, a paleoecologist can contribute to neoecology in the matter of origin of adaptations and other problems, as he is in a position to apply here his knowledge of extinct organisms.

Acquaintance with *biogeography* (*zoogeography* and *phytogeography*) is of great importance to a paleoecologist.

The corresponding data in the domain of paleontology have been, as yet, only poorly worked out, although they are very important and wide open for exploration.

The older the organisms with which a paleontologist works, the more difficult it is to utilize the data on living organisms for elucidation of the ecology of the fossils. Whereas it is quite possible to utilize (more or less directly) data on living forms when studying Cenozoic faunas and floras, and permissible to do so in investigating some Mesozoic organisms, the actualistic method is of little use in studies of Paleozoic animals and plants. However, in this case a paleontologist is helped by the phenomenon of *"vicariousness* in time." This provides a lead for his quest not in the direction of related forms, but in that of structurally analogous forms, becoming convergent because of similar habitat conditions and similar modes of life. This fruitful approach has been utilized only slightly up to the present. For instance, we might compare Lower Carboniferous productids of the genus *Gigantoproductus* with Mesozoic and Cenozoic oysters. Both led sedentary lives in shallow turbulent waters, possessed similar, cup-and-cover shape of shells, and grew gregariously in banks. Another productid, *Irboskites* from the Upper Devonian of the "Main Devonian Field" (main Devonian outcrop area in Russian Platform), lived attached to rocky bottoms, pebbles, and shells of other invertebrates also in turbulent shallow waters. Its shape is convergent with that of *Balanus*, a sedentary crustacean of ancient and modern seas. The convergence resulted from life in analogous conditions.

Ecological peculiarities of some fossil forms which have no relatives among living forms, or which lack any clear-cut analogies among them, present considerable difficulties in making interpretations; in such cases a morphofunctional analysis of the skeletal remains becomes particularly useful. One should also utilize *other components* of the paleobiocoenoses studied which may yield more easily to paleoecological analysis; their study may help to elucidate the paleoecological peculiarities of the more difficult forms, as both may bear one and the same "seal of environment" (see p. 18).

5. CONCEPTS AND TERMINOLOGY

Life media are composed of *abiotic (inorganic: physical* and *chemical*) and *biotic* (*organic: biological*) *factors,* or *components*. Such factors in the geological past have reached us only partially. In utilizing these fragmentary and incomplete data, which give a hint as to inorganic and organic elements of ancient life, we must attempt to reconstruct it as fully as possible. The factors of the two categories are interconnected intimately, and are parts of the whole medium and life unit. Consequently, the study of one kind of factor helps to understand the other kind: abiotic factors cannot be understood fully without a study of biotic factors, and vice versa.

The biotic components of a life medium comprise all its organisms in the course of their lifetime, including their influence upon the surrounding medium, organic as well as inorganic.

Abiotic components include the factors which determine and compose the physical and chemical regime of a given habitat (sea-bottom sediment, salinity and temperature of water, etc.), as well as the hard parts of the dead animals (shells, bones, teeth, etc.), which become parts of a sediment. The excreta (for instance, coprolites) and the products of decomposition of the soft organic tissues belong to a special category.

Depending on their ability to tolerate this or that factor, and as a quantitative indication of this tolerance, organisms are labeled by special terms with prefixes *oligo-, meso-,* and *poly-,* which denote their tolerance to small, medium, or large amounts of a given factor (for instance, oligo-, meso-, and polyhaline animals).

It is also necessary to determine the maxima and minima of each factor under which an organism can exist. In some organisms the range between maximum and minimum for a given factor is broad, and in others it is narrow. According to this the organisms are differentiated as *eurybiontic* (adapted to a great range of a given factor) and *stenobiontic* (adapted to only a small, possibly insignificant fluctuation of this factor), as indicated in Table 1.

Also used is terminology indicative of the "love" or "fear" shown by an organism in relation to a given factor.

Table 1

Environmental factors and terms for organisms
widely or narrowly adapted to them

Factor	Organism
Biotope	Eurytopic, stenotopic
Depth	Eurybathic, stenobathic
Salinity	Euryhaline, stenohaline
Temperature	Eurythermal, stenothermal

This leads to classifying organisms in such groups as *halophilous* and *halophobous*, for instance.

In this manner, when undertaking to reconstruct the life conditions of different forms or groups of organisms and biocoenoses, a paleoecologist must elucidate not only the conditions in which they were usually encountered, but also the conditions where they were found only in small number, as well as limitations beyond which their life would be impossible. In other words, it is necessary to strive for complete "mapping" of the relationships between the objects studied and all habitat factors. Having these goals in mind, it is necessary when studying certain deposits to investigate not only the beds in which the forms or complex of forms and biocoenoses of interest to us are encountered, but also the beds or exposures characterized by other kinds of forms or biocoenoses alternating with them, as well as those which are quite unfossiliferous. As a result of such comparative study it becomes possible to establish the most and the least favorable conditions for existence of a certain form or a complex of forms, and conditions under which their life was impossible.

Because the life of organisms in certain conditions has been dependent on a number of factors (salinity, temperature, depth, substrate, etc.), we should strive toward establishing the influence of each factor on each form and its distribution, and do this quantitatively.

Paleoecological analysis can and should deal with the whole world of fossil organisms of any geological age—organisms that inhabited any environment and had any mode of life. In doing so we should be aware of the fact, however, that there is a great difference in the possibilities afforded to paleoecological analysis when applied to terrestrial and water inhabitants, to vertebrates and invertebrates, and to free and sedentary forms.

Let us indicate the differences which are involved in paleoecological investigations concerned, on the one hand, with marine invertebrates and their remains, and, on the other, with terrestrial vertebrates and their remains.

Table 2

Paleoecological comparison of marine and nonmarine organic assemblages

Marine invertebrates	Terrestrial vertebrates
Many sluggish or sedentary; generally good preservation of skeletal remains.	Mobile; remains generally fragmentary.
Characteristic: mass occurrence and wide distribution of remains.	Characteristic: rare occurrence and narrowly localized accumulation of remains.
Place of burial coincident with place of habitat.	Place of burial commonly different from place of habitat.
Biocoenoses predominant.	Thanatocoenoses predominant.
Comparatively simple, usually outer skeleton, armor, or shell, which frequently gives insufficient information on animal's organization, and consequently about its life conditions.	Complex inner ossified skeleton, which reflects animal's organization fairly well, allowing satisfactory interpretation of its appearance and life conditions.

The peculiarities indicated have determined the various exploratory paths which were followed, for instance, by

V. O. Kovalevskiy, who investigated Tertiary ruminants, and, on the other hand, by N. I. Andrusov, who studied Tertiary marine molluscan faunas. The same peculiarities are also reflected in the content and direction of investigations in our time, although nowadays, thanks to the development of new, accessory branches of science and work methods (taphonomy with biostratinomy, paleoecological-lithological analysis), the difference in former approaches to the study of terrestrial vertebrates and marine invertebrates is somewhat reduced.

As noted above, a paleoecologist should differentiate between the *place of habitat* of an organism and the *place of its burial*, and in some instances also the *place of its death*. These may coincide, but quite frequently they differ. In any case, a bed containing organic remains represents the location and medium of their burial, but it remains to be proved whether the fossil-bearing bed originated where the organisms lived, or in the place where they perished.

It is particularly important to differentiate the places of life, death, and burial when studying terrestrial vertebrates, remains of which are indicated by investigations as occurring most frequently in delta deposits, where they have been carried by rivers. For example, in the well-known North Dvina locality Lower Permian amphibians and reptiles are regarded as belonging to submerged levels of the river delta. Here the animal carcasses carried down by the river ultimately came to be buried; these animals could also have perished not where they lived, but in a water torrent at a spring inundation. The faunal assemblage in the Upper Jurassic Solnhofen locality in Germany represents a more complex origin. Here, in the calcareous ooze, many marine animals which happened to enter the lagoon from the sea at high water perished and were buried, and in similar manner death overtook various terrestrial animals which walked in, flew in, or were carried into the lagoon from the land by rivers or by strong winds. Among all the fauna revealed in the Solnhofen shales, only several species of insects (a stick-bug, which lived on the water surface, and water bugs) were actually inhabitants of the lagoon.

Because of the need to study peculiarities in the burial of animal remains, a new scientific discipline called

biostratinomy appeared in the 1930's* (Weigelt, 1927a).
The object of biostratinomy is elucidation of mechanisms
in the tridimensional disposition of organic remains within
a sedimentary layer, and in the relations of each to others.
Problems of the biostratinomy of marine faunas have been
considered in many studies undertaken by scientists of
U.S.S.R. (Gekker, Ivanova, Merklin, Makridin, Vassoevich,
and others).

Elucidation of the conditions and peculiarities of burial
of fossil organisms are particularly important to paleontologists who study the remains of terrestrial animals
and plants, because these are usually not buried in the
place of their habitat. An initial study of these problems
as related to terrestrial vertebrates has been made by
I. A. Efremov, who introduced the new name *taphonomy*
for the scientific discipline concerned with the manner of
burial and the origin of accumulations of animal and plant
remains.

Although taphonomy is of considerable importance to
paleoecologists, it is not a part of paleoecology; taphonomy
concerns dead organisms *and the problems of their burial,*
whereas paleoecology concerns ancient organisms in their
life relationships. Biostratinomy is a part of taphonomy.

It is important for a paleoecologist to ascertain which
organisms in a given bed were already dead when deposited,
thus being a part of clastic material, and which composed
a biocoenosis at the place of deposition. It is also necessary to determine whether we are dealing with the
remains of a life association of organisms (that is,
with an ancient biocoenosis, or *paleobiocoenosis* **) or

---

*From stratum (Latin) = layer. Under biostratinomic mechanisms we now
include only the post-mortem manner of disposing of organic remains which
differs from their disposition during life; the latter mechanisms we class as
paleoecological.

**Some authors suggest the term "paleocoenosis" (Merklin, 1950) instead
of paleobiocoenosis, to underscore the fact that because of incompleteness of
the geological record a paleontologist cannot restore and understand an ancient
biocoenosis as completely as is possible for a contemporary biocoenosis by a
zoologist or botanist. It seems that this overly cautious concern about a term
for designation of an ancient biocoenosis is superfluous, as it is well known that
the possibilities afforded to paleontologists for reconstruction and understanding of ancient life are more restricted than the possibilities open to zoologists
and botanists for understanding of the world of living organisms. Thus we use
the terms "paleozoology," "paleobotany," "paleoecology," "paleopathology,"
etc.

with an accumulation of organic remains merely buried together, that is with a fossil thanatocoenosis, or *paleo-thanatocoenosis*.

The concept of biocoenosis has been defined by several Soviet ecologists (Zernov, 1913, 1949; Gur'yanova et al., 1930; Kashkarov, 1945; Vorob'ev, 1949). Biocoenosis* is a term designating the population of a limited part of a life medium formed in the course of a fairly prolonged span of time under the influence of biotic and abiotic factors. This results in the establishment of certain relationships, structures, and numerical ratios between the separate members of the population. Biocoenoses do not remain constant, since changes in the environment during geological time exercise changing influences on them.

The term *biotope* designates a limited area characterized by certain physical and chemical peculiarities which determine the conditions under which the existence of a certain biocoenosis is possible. In connection with variability within the factors that characterize a biotope, a biocoenosis may be divided into *associations* of species which occupy different parts of a biotope and are characterized by different quantitative relationships between the species. According to Merklin's classification (Merklin, 1950), species may be *dominant* (with number of individuals exceeding 50% of all species), *characteristic* (with number of individuals exceeding 25% of all species), *associate* (with number of individuals exceeding 10%), and *incidental* (with number less than 10%, or only isolated individuals encountered). Thus, for instance, the bottom of the Tarkhan sea, in the region of the present Kerch Peninsula, at one time was inhabited by a biocoenosis which may be called *Cardium-Lima-Aloidis* biocoenosis. In this biocoenosis may be differentiated a *Cardium liverovskayae* Merkl.-*Lima skeliensis* Merkl.-*Musculus conditus* Mayer association which inhabited a clayey bottom with admixture of silt. Among these *Cardium* was a dominant form, and the species *Lima* and *Musculus* characteristic; besides these, in this biocoenosis were identified 7 associated and 11 incidental pelecypod forms, and also associated and incidental gastropods, pteropods, ophiuroids, crabs, ostracodes, annelids, bryozoans and

*From koinos (Greek) = general, common. The concept was defined and the name introduced by the German zoologist Moebius in 1877.

foraminifers. Somewhat different conditions existed in neighboring parts of the bottom, where deposits consisted of sandy silt and a large amount of shell detritus; here lived a different association of the same biocoenosis: *Aloidis gibba* Ol., *Abra parabilis* Zhizh. var. *attalica* Merkl., *Cuspidaria cuspidata* Ol., *Cultellus papyraceus* Reuss var. *scaphoideus* Zhizh. The first of these species was dominant and others characteristic of the association. To this same assemblage belonged as associate and incidental forms the above-mentioned species of pelecypods *Cardium, Lima, Musculus* and others, associate and incidental species of gastropods and other invertebrates.

It may be added here that because it is necessary to conduct paleoecological investigations in as great detail as possible, though paleoecological problems are as yet insufficiently clarified, it would be wrong to plan exact itineraries, with certain distances to be covered over a certain period of time; but a reported length of an elaborate columnar section and a number of studied exposures may, to some extent, serve as a basis for evaluating the amount of completed investigations.

Different organisms living in various parts of a sea bottom need different sorts of food. Because of this, they lead different modes of life, some burrowing, others attaching themselves, a third kind lying freely, a fourth moving around, and so on. Correspondingly, they pursue different means of procuring food, have different peculiarities in propagation, different adaptations for defense against enemies or injurious influences of abiotic factors, etc. Because of this, the population of a single biocoenosis may be represented by very different *adaptive types*, or *life forms*, and these, as it is customary to say, occupy *different ecological niches* within one and the same biotope. However, some peculiarities of a given biotope (water turbulence, depth, bottom character, etc.) usually make also a common impression (*"seal of environment"*) upon all members of a single biocoenosis. For instance, in a bottom of fine-grained sediments and in conditions of only gentle water disturbance, the shells of mollusks are thinner and lighter than the thick, larger shells of mollusks which live and have lived in shallower conditions in coarser sediments in the belt of turbulent waters. Other examples: those representatives of all classes of echinoderms (e.g., echinoids, crinoids, starfishes, ophiuroids, holothurians) which inhabit oozy bottoms at great depths in modern oceans thus have very weakly developed calcareous skeletons, and many dwellers in bathyal depths, belonging to all kinds of animal groups, are luminescent.

Thus, different members of a biocoenosis bear some common traits, not because of kinship but because of adaptation to common life conditions.

We should strive to determine whether we are dealing with a fossil biocoenosis in its pure form, that is, without admixture of members belonging to other biocoenoses. In the case of such mixture we should endeavor to ascertain how many biocoenoses are represented in the assemblage of forms under study; further, it should be ascertained whether all of the encountered organic remains were buried outside of the biotopes of these biocoenoses or within the habitat of one of them, and so on. Such analysis of accumulated organic remains is essential because without it one might readily accept as cohabitants organisms which have been merely buried together.

It is not always easy to determine whether organic remains encountered together were members of a single fossil biocoenosis. In case of doubt, it is recommended that the more general, noncommittal term *"complex of forms"* should be used.

The term *thanatocoenosis** and concepts associated with it were introduced by the German hydrobiologist E. Wasmund (1926) in order to distinguish accumulations of dead organisms originating under the influence of entirely different mechanisms than the associations of living organisms.

At first, paleontologists applied the term thanatocoenosis to any kind of accumulation of dead organisms not formed during the life of a single biocoenosis. Subsequently, some investigators narrowed the concept of thanatocoenosis to signify only assemblages of dead organisms brought together prior to their burial ("associations of the dead"). The concept was restricted still more by scientists who suggested that the term should be applied only to accumulated remnants of organisms which perished

*From thanatos (Greek) = death.

together from a common cause. In 1927 the German paleontologist W. Quenstedt introduced the term *taphocoenosis*
("burial association")* to indicate cemeteries of organisms or of their remains prior to petrification (Quenstedt,
1927).

Other concepts and terms have been introduced for
various "associations"** (necrocoenosis, liptocoenosis,
oryctocoenosis, etc.). These show that their authors at-
tempted to differentiate *1*) recent associations from fossil
ones; *2*) associations of different origin depending on: *a*)
topographic evidence of a single habitat or of several,
b) cause of death being single or varied, and *c*) time of
origin of the associations, single or varied; *3*) distinction
among perished organisms of those which came to be
buried; *4*) among organisms buried, those which have
reached us as fossils, and so on.

The abundance of recently introduced concepts and
new terms indicates rapid growth of this science, which
is also indicated by an observed lack of uniformity in the
use of the same terms by different investigators. Therefore, a current task should be the achievement of greater
precision in defining each concept and in determining the
significance of each term. It may be added here that success in paleoecological work depends to a considerable
extent on maximum differentiation of our approach to each
phenomenon. However, creation of numerous new terms
(especially those derived from unfamiliar Greek and Latin
words) is inadmissible. A way out of this dilemma is
adoption of designations consisting of a few commonly
used vernacular words.

In order to penetrate farthest into life problems of extinct organisms, a paleontologist should investigate the
causes and conditions of their death.

Besides old age and disease, death could be due to
quite different causes, such as attack by other animals,
invasion by parasites, overgrowth by other animals and
plants, lack of sufficient oxygen, entrapment in some
viscous medium (ooze, asphalt, tar, quagmire, and others),

---

*From taphos (Greek) = grave, burial.
**Under the term "associations" are here understood various groups of
dead organisms exclusively, or groups of remains of dead organisms mixed
with dropped-off parts of living organisms.

lowered water level and desiccation of a basin, or contrariwise drowning in floods, and so on. In some cases one may observe (e.g., in amber) evidence of the death struggle of animals.

In many instances some proof of this or that cause of death may be detected. These should be described and explained. Paleoecologists should be acquainted with processes which operate under different conditions on the carcasses of animals and remains of plants (the domain of *necrology*), up to the stage of their complete fossilization.

Fossilized remains may bear indications of the processes of decomposition. For example, some cephalopod shells have been lifted from their original burial in ooze by gases of decomposition of their soft parts; the scaly integument of ganoid fishes has been found inflated and burst, and various stages of decomposition and destruction of the body and skeleton of fishes occasionally have been observable from features of their fossilized remains.

The hard skeletal parts and secreted protective coverings of animals (e.g., worm tubes) are subject to the action of chemical, mechanical, and biological agencies both during the life of the animals that produced them and subsequent to the burial of remains. Oxygen and carbon dioxide are chemical agencies which cause dissolution; water and wind are mechanical agencies which tend to destroy the hard skeletal structures by rolling, in the course of which they are polished, abraded, or broken, whereas flexible bodies are merely bent (Plate II, 2). Further, dismemberment and mechanical sorting of skeletal remains by size, weight, and shape may be brought about; concavo-convex shells may come to be oriented in their most stable position with the convex side up (Plate I, 3 and 4), elongated shells and other remains being disposed in subparallel position (Plate II, 1 and 3).

Among biological agencies acting upon hard skeletal structures are micro- and macroorganisms, which bore mechanically or etch chemically into them; such are boring algae and mollusks (Plate III, 1, 4, and 5), boring worms (Plate III, 2 and 3), and boring sponges (Plate III, 6). Here also belong various animals which bite through or crush shells and carapaces in order to reach the soft body of their victims, carnivores which gnaw and crush bones, and so on.

The problems of *fossilization* are also very important to paleoecologists (see Deecke, 1923).

6. PALEOECOLOGY AND GEOLOGICAL PROBLEMS

Many factors of the life surroundings of ancient faunas, such as depth, temperature and disturbance of water in a given basin, which are easily determined by a hydrologist or even by a biologist himself working on the modern organic world, cannot be directly observed and estimated by a geologist or paleoecologist. We are compelled to elucidate the data which characterize these factors in an indirect way, resorting to a lithological and faciological analysis. In doing so, just as in the case of a study of fossil organisms, we should not limit ourselves to mere description and precise determination of rock strata under study but must ascertain the conditions of their origin, thus restoring to a considerable extent the environment of their contained fauna and flora. Furthermore, special attention should be paid to processes which change sediments subsequent to their deposition (diagenesis, epigenesis); these changes should be eliminated in attempting to reconstruct depositional conditions.

Paleoecological and lithological investigations need to be conducted side by side. A paleoecologist cannot escape the realm of lithological investigations, nor, vice versa, a lithologist the realm of paleoecology, because occasionally only in the contiguous domain will they be able to find a key to the solution of a number of problems in their respective fields — problems of the mode and conditions of organic life, on the one hand, and the nature of sedimentary deposition on the other. It is self-evident that a paleoecologist, as well as a lithologist, must be also a good geologist. In view of the specialization of scientific disciplines, with vigorous and continuous growth of factual materials accumulated in different scientific domains, and in view of the differentiation of working methods, particularly in laboratories, it is impossible for a single person to master equally well all branches of knowledge required for work in paleoecology and lithology.

Because of this, a research worker is compelled to become either a sedimentary petrologist or a paleoecologist, and for an exhaustive study of materials he must work with a specialist in the other realm. Nevertheless, it is highly desirable that the paleoecologist himself acquire as complete knowledge as possible for independent grasp of all data gathered.

The solution of problems encountered in paleoecology thus calls for specialists with a wide range, and it is also necessary to work out a method of combined *paleoecological-lithological* investigations of ancient deposits. The suggested designation of this method does not include all divisions of paleontology and geology which may be involved in the working out of paleoecological problems, but only the basic, leading divisions, i.e., paleoecology and lithology.

Following the customary elucidation of the qualitative composition of the fauna and flora and the nature of the enclosing rocks (generic and specific composition of the fauna and flora and, correspondingly, the types of rocks) and their quantitative characteristics, it behooves the paleoecologist and lithologist to determine jointly—in studying an ancient sea bottom and its organic content, for instance—how far from a shore line is the part of the ancient sea bottom investigated and its population, its illumination, depth, degree of water disturbance and temperature, gaseous regime, salinity, and other factors of the medium which are investigated by hydrologists and oceanographers in the modern seas.

At present we are far from able to determine exactly many of the general and local peculiarities just listed, but sooner or later we shall learn to recognize them on the evidence of the same materials which are being studied now, namely, the geological sections, the rocks and the fossils which together reflect the combination of physical, chemical, and biotic conditions of past environments in which the ancient organic world lived and developed and in which its remnants became buried.

The foundation for the combined paleoecological-lithological method of investigation is the geological section, utilized differently by geologists and paleontologists, and requiring particularly elaborate and diverse studies when investigated paleoecologically. Paleoecological conclusions may be properly established only on detailed and many-sided study of a section.

The earth's crust is structurally divided into different parts: platforms, geosynclines, foothill flexures and intermountain depressions, all of which differ from each other in degree of mobility, types of sediments, tempo of their deposition, thickness, and many other respects. All these regions, which differ in geological structure, permit application of paleoecological investigations; however, these cannot be undertaken with equal ease, and the results obtained will not be equally definite in different regions.

Conditions favorable for paleoecological analysis and for elucidation of the life conditions of fossil organisms may be enumerated as follows: *a*) good exposures which allow little doubt as to correct correlation of sections and which make detailed field observations possible, accompanied by large collections of fossils; *b*) good preservation of fauna and flora, together with feasibility of extracting the fossils from rock satisfactorily, and absence of metamorphic changes; *c*) comparatively small thickness of strata studied, allowing observation of separate horizons in individual outcrops or determination of uninterrupted stratigraphic successions from separate exposures; *d*) substantial horizontal extent of a formation which permits recognition of facies changes within each layer; and *e*) insignificance of tectonic disturbances or their total absence, so that deposits can be traced for long distances without gaps.

All of the enumerated favorable conditions characterize marine deposits on continental platforms. Geosynclinal deposits, with their greatly increased thickness and commonly developed metamorphic changes associated with strong tectonic disturbances, are more difficult subjects of investigation. Those who are undertaking paleoecological investigations for the first time should choose relatively easy study objectives at first, and later on more difficult ones. This relates to fossiliferous formations as well as to different organic forms, faunas, and floras.

Most advantageous for paleoecological analysis are series consisting of *interbedded layers* of different lithologic composition, and, in connection with this, different faunal and floral complexes. Such series reflect great variability of conditions of sedimentation and of life environments. They offer a paleoecologist more data for judgments as to the conditions and modes of life of extinct animals and plants than do deposits of monotonous sediments with equally monotonous faunas and floras (Figure 1).

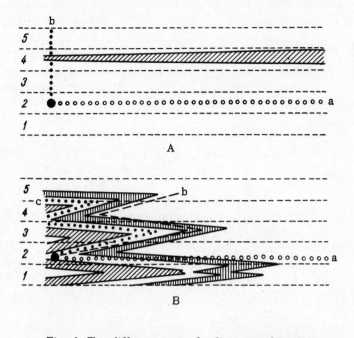

Fig. 1. Two different types of sedimentary deposits.
A—Monotonous facies and biocoenoses, which existed for a
long time in the same place. B—Different and continuously
migrating facies and biocoenoses.
Successive time divisions during which deposition of sediments and life of organisms have taken place are indicated
by numerals, and their boundaries by dotted lines. a, b and
c indicate different directions along which comparative
paleoecological investigations were conducted.

A series of beds with *alternating lithologically different
characters* offer an investigator greater comparative
material and provide a good opportunity both to delineate
the life possibilities of extinct animals and to determine
their correspondence to particular facies. Furthermore,
sediments of this type are distinguished not only by radical
(usually abrupt) changes of facies in vertical succession
but also by fairly abrupt facies changes along their lateral
extent, a situation which permits verification and elabora-
tion of conclusions reached from study of columnar
sections.

It should be pointed out, however, that in such greatly
varying deposits it is difficult to gather material for
analysis of the phylogenetic development of organisms,

because in a given part of a basin, on account of abrupt changes in organic environment, a given fauna or flora could not have existed very long. A series deposited under such conditions, for instance those of the Upper Devonian within the Main Devonian Field (Figure 1B), will enclose only isolated, disconnected segments of phylogenetic branches.

The situation would have been different in parts of a basin where depositional conditions varied less abruptly and rapidly (Figure 1A). Here deposits are lithologically more uniform and contain remains of organisms which developed uninterruptedly in the same place for a considerable length of time. Therefore, this sort of sedimentation will furnish good material for elucidation of the development of some groups of organisms, particularly eurybiontic, and also for defining continuous phylogenetic lineages and complete phylogenetic trees. Deposits of the Upper Devonian of the Main Devonian Field, Ordovician of the Leningrad and Estonian regions, Carboniferous of the central part of the Russian Platform (Figures 26 and 27), and some stages of the Paleogene of the Fergana depression afford examples.

The experience of Soviet scientists indicates that *combined paleoecological-lithological investigations of complete basins of the geological past, or of their substantial parts over long stretches of geological time* (preferably during the entire time of the basin's existence), *are the most fruitful.* The enormous factual materials obtained provide ample possibilities for comparative analysis and verification of paleoecological conclusions.

Such broadly conceived investigations make possible numerous well-substantiated conclusions on systematics and evolution of the organic world, lithogenesis, facies, paleogeography, paleoclimatology, stratigraphy, tectonics, genesis of mineral deposits, and on other subjects illuminated from a paleoecological viewpoint.

Thus, for instance, some major mistakes have been made in past correlations of various sections, up to and including stages. The errors were committed by investigators whose studies ignored the influence of facies and the succession of fossil faunas and floras in relation to facies — i.e., who were ignorant of the fundamental principles of paleoecology. A good example of difficulties encountered in correlating varied facies of marine deposits and errors introduced because of them is provided by Upper Devonian deposits of the Main Devonian Field in the European U.S.S.R.

Different types of rocks with different complexes of organic forms are developed in the sections of various marine deposits in the western and the eastern halves of this Main Devonian Field; besides this, in its central part the exposures are insufficiently complete to allow tracing of transitions of facies within the area. The almost complete absence of common organic forms in contemporaneous deposits that differ in facies has led to divergent correlations of sections in the two halves of the Main Devonian Field. A unified stratigraphy applicable to deposits of the whole region could be worked out only after establishment in the eastern half of the field of regularities in the changes of facies (both sediments and organic complexes) from the shores toward deep parts of the basin. In this way it has been determined that the assemblage of organisms characteristic of the western part of the region provides *successive links* in a single contemporaneous set of organic complexes. Figure 2 illustrates the arrangement of this ''gamma'' series of organic assemblages and of the rocks which enclose them. Figure 3 is a summarized paleoecological profile (general section) across the whole extent of the Main Devonian Field.

One may observe, therefore, that what formerly encumbered the work of a stratigrapher was peculiarities which could have been predicted if the data at hand had been considered from a paleoecological viewpoint.

The cited example of correlation of dissimilar geological sections of the Devonian of the Russian Platform which are difficult to compare demonstrates the paramount importance of paleoecology in solving problems of *stratigraphy*. When the basic stratigraphic method of ''index fossils'' or the presently recommended method of ''index assemblages'' cannot be applied, then the *method of correlation of sections on the evidence of ecological succession in space of form complexes and biocoenoses* comes to the fore.

Study of series composed of very variable facies which abruptly replace each other in space indicates that the greater the difference between facies, the fewer are the

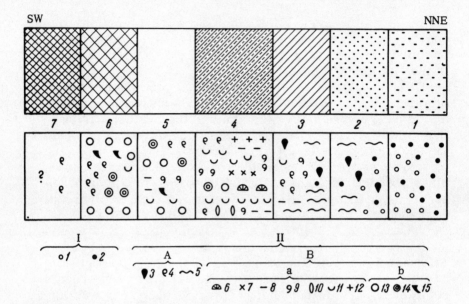

Fig. 2. Regular set of succession ("gamma") of rocks and organic form complexes associated with them in marine and near-shore continental deposits of Upper Devonian of Main Devonian Field in north-northeast to southwest direction (from seashore to deep waters).
Legend: 1—red terrigenous rocks; 2—white quartz sands; 3—clays; 4—clayey limestones and marls; 5—limestones; 6—dolomitic limestones; 7—dolomites. Fanuna and flora: I—inhabitants of fresh water: 1—*Trochilisca*; 2—fishes of red-bed facies. II—inhabitants of sea: A—euryhaline forms: 3—*Lingula*; 4—*Platyschisma*; 5—traces of worms. B—stenohaline forms: a—inhabitants of waters with normal salinity: 6—*Tabulata*; 7—*Spirorbis*; 8—pelecypods; 9—mostly gastropods; 10—nautiloids; 11—mostly articulate brachiopods; 12—crinoids. b—inhabitants of waters with normal and somewhat greater salinity: 13—blue-green algae, *Girvanella, Pycnostroma*; 14—stromatoporoids; 15—*Rugosa* corals.

forms of organisms common to them; it is well known that contemporaneous facies may have no organic forms at all in common. Accordingly, a stratigrapher not infrequently encounters problems analogous to the one just discussed, where correlation of sections requires study of regularities in the changes of faunas and floras in space dependent on conditions of their existence.

Let us consider other cases. Whenever a stratigrapher is engaged in a particularly detailed bed-by-bed correlation of formations that represent a small span of geological time in the course of which the species content of a

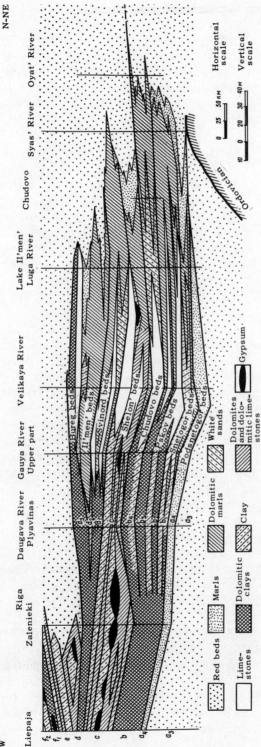

Fig. 3. Composite lithologic-stratigraphic profile across the whole Main Devonian Field.

SW

Liepaja

Riga
Zalenieki

Daugava River
Plyavinas

Gauya River
Upper part

Velikaya River

Lake Il'men'
Luga River

Chudovo   Syas' River   Oyat' River

N-NE

f_2
f_1
e
d
c
b
a_4
a_3

Bureg beds
Il'men' beds
Svinord beds
Shelon' beds
Chudovo beds
P.skov beds
Snetogor beds
Podsnetogor beds

d
c
b
a
a_3

Ordovician

Horizontal
scale

Vertical
scale

0   25   50 км

10

0   20   30   40 м

Red beds

Lime-
stones

Marls

Dolomitic
clays

Dolomitic
marls

Clay

White
sands

Dolomites
and dolo-
mitic lime-
stones

Gypsum

fauna (or flora) has not changed substantially, he will be obliged to abandon the method of studying index fossils and index assemblages and adopt another method, namely the *method of detailed correlation of sections on the basis of paleoecological and biostratinomical evidence.* Paleoecological evidence includes the following: quantitative relationships of species during their life; their belonging to particular parts of a rock layer, corresponding to the place and time of their actual life; various traces of animals and their location in particular levels of a bed; the orientation of shells and roots of plants indicative of position in life, and so on. Biostratinomical evidence includes secondary, post-mortem relationships of various organic remains, as well as the preservation of shells, their orientations, their accumulations, and so on, determined by mechanical factors which operated at the time of their death or subsequent to it.

Figure 4 shows part of a section of the Lower Carboniferous on the Msta River in the Novgorod region, which includes eight beds of limestone with faunal remains, the general specific content of which changes negligibly throughout the whole section. This composite section could not be drawn up from a single exposure, and in putting it together, part by part from many exposures, errors in correlation of some of the beds were introduced. It was possible to recognize all of the beds in separate exposures and thus compose the whole section correctly only through use of the above-listed paleoecological and biostratinomical features, here restricted to comparatively short distance (several kilometers).

The Msta section has demonstrated clearly that the enumerated peculiarities can serve as excellent guides for bed-by-bed correlations of sections, particularly in those cases when they consist of frequently repeated sequences of several rock types with correspondingly recurring organic assemblages. This method can render good service in detailed, bed-by-bed stratigraphy of mineral deposits.

The method of differentiating stratigraphic units and correlating sections on the basis of changes of ecological complexes in time may be recommended to stratigraphers also. Specific changes in specific contents in faunas and floras in the course of geological time—whereas their ecological aspects remain the same—are not the only phenomena

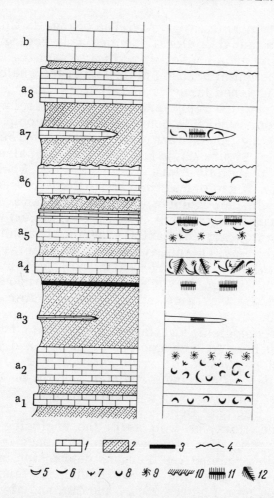

Fig. 4. Section of Lower Carboniferous deposits on Msta River abve town of Borovichi showing differences in paleoecological and biostratigraphical characteristics of eight limestone beds (a_1-a_8) with faunas containing the same species.

Legend: Lithology of interstratified rocks shown in column at left, fossils in column at right. 1—limestone; 2—sandy-clayey rocks; 3—coal; 4—erosion surface; 5—*Gigantoproductus* with both valves connected; 6—*Gigantoproductus* with isolated valves; 7—*Productus semiplanus* Schwetz.; 8—small brachiopods; 9—passages of *Zoophycos Taonurus, Spirophyton*; 10—looplike and small, simple worm borings; 11—horizontal stigmaria; 12—vertical and oblique stigmaria. Symbols for brachiopods show also their orientation, those for *Gigantoproductus* indicating also whole shells and isolated valves.

important in biostratigraphy. The change in time (in sections) of a faunal or floral complex as to ecological aspect is very important also, providing this change embraces fairly substantial areas. For instance, the Shelon' horizon was distinguished during preparation of stratigraphic scales because, with the representation of lagoon sedimentation, it was extremely poor in complex forms in comparison with the preceding Chudovo and subsequent Svinord marine complexes (see Figure 22). In just the same way paleoecological analysis of the late Alai fauna of Fergana, when traced in the course of geological time, led to the disclosure of a peculiar molluscan complex, very poor in genera and species, which characterizes this interval of time and which indicates a temporary substantial lowering of salinity of waters in Fergana Bay. On this evidence the Upper Alai substage has been divided into three parts: $Al\frac{1}{2}$, $Al\frac{2}{2}$, and $Al\frac{3}{2}$ (see Figure 21), though previously, because the upper and lower parts contain the same index forms of oysters, it had not been divided.

Paleoecological and taphonomical data provide considerable help to both geological theory and practice in studying *conditions of sedimentation and formation of mineral deposits having a sedimentary origin.*

Following are examples from Paleogene deposits of the Fergana region. Detailed paleoecological study of its fauna and flora, as well as of the enclosing sediments, allowed recognition of several benthic zones in the marine bay which occupied the Fergana depression in Paleogene times, each zone and facies having its characteristic population (see Figures 23, 24 and 29), and also permitted differentiation of various parts of the bay (northern, southern, area in front of the bay entrance, etc.). This study also contributed significantly to greater precision in determining depositional conditions of the various types of marine and lagoonal sediments.

It has been established that besides several previously known marine and salt-lagoon deposits along the periphery of the basin, there is a great development of deltaic red beds to the north, formerly classified as Cretaceous.

The deltaic deposits are replaced toward the center of the basin by terrigenous and carbonate-detrital sediments containing remains of marine mollusks, claws of crustaceans, and numerous holes of burrowing animals. Study of the borings and claws indicates that they belong to burrowing marine decapods of the genus *Callianassa*, modern representatives of which inhabit the littoral (marsh zone) and upper sublittoral belt of warm seas.

Consequently, study of these remains of crustaceans and holes bored by them, which formerly were entirely neglected, has permitted reliable recognition of the littoral deposits and precise tracing of the shore line of the Fergana Bay for all stages of its geological history. These observations, as well as determination of the Paleogene age of the red beds, have much economic value, since they permit mapping of the natural boundaries of marine deposits which contain various useful minerals.

Study of the rocks and faunas of the Fergana Gulf has also led to understanding the conditions that control origin of the dolomitic oozes, which were converted into dolomites, encountered at two horizons in the Fergana geological section. The conclusion is reached that these oozes were precipitated during periods of substantial reduction of salinity in the bay, when it was inhabited by an impoverished molluscan fauna—small *Eulima, Meretrix tschangirtaschensis* Liwer., with *Unio* appearing also. In this way a new type of dolomite-producing basin has been recognized—a marine embayment in an arid region containing water substantially freshened by the influx of rivers.

Comparison of observations on the appearance and disappearance of various ecological faunal assemblages in the Paleogene section of Fergana with observations on petroleum occurrences in this region has shown that the levels of mass accumulations of the mollusks mentioned coincide with maximum oil saturation. Consequently this association of forms in the Fergana Paleogene characterizes conditions favorable for accumulation of petroleum-producing organic remains. Therefore, this and other similar relationships can serve effectively as guides for oil exploration in analogous geological situations encountered in other regions.

Experience proves that systematic paleontology and paleoecology can provide for practical use not only index fossils (genera, species, and entire assemblages) illustrated in suitable atlases and explained in accompanying text, adapted for determining the geological age of sedimentary rocks, but also such fossils, likewise arranged in atlases and manuals, suited for the recognition of facies, conditions of sedimentary deposition, and formation of minerals associated with sedimentary deposits.

Such "index fossils," in the new sense of the term, actually exist: it is only necessary to differentiate them. This can be done in the course of a developing paleoecological research, or better, combined paleoecological-lithological investigations. Reliable facies indicators derived from them can be defined for each geological system and various ancient basins. Then, from integration of data furnished by many basins, it will become possible to distinguish generally useful *"indicators of facies and of conditions affecting deposition of sediments and the formation of mineral deposits,"* utilizing evidence of fossil forms, ecological complexes, biocoenoses, and the evidence of regularities of their burial. Such compendia are apt to be very useful in prospecting for various mineral deposits of sedimentary origin (combustible and noncombustible, metallic and nonmetallic, and building materials).

Finally, observations on paleobiogeography and paleo-ecology, and in some cases on taphonomy, facilitate establishing *a general outline of the tectonic history of an area, including small oscillations of the earth's crust, their time of origin and duration of the "activity" of tectonic structures, as well as determination of the original orientation of beds.*

As a matter of fact, the changes in the animal and plant world reflect (and thus register) the changes in their environment which are largely due to displacements in the earth's crust. The observable shifting of faunas and floras in a columnar section, and their migrations in space and time, can be considered primarily as consequences of tectonic processes which affected a given area or regions adjacent to it. In this way tectonic processes have been "recorded," as it were, by the composition and development of the organic world.

Detailed investigations of certain tectonic structures have disclosed that they were active for a long time, and that they were expressed on the sea bottom as elevations prior to their final development. Coarser sediments were usually deposited over the summit and on the slopes of such elevations, with finer ones beyond these limits.

Faunas and floras inhabiting these different areas were correspondingly different, and conditions of their burial were dissimilar. Thus, discovery in contemporaneous deposits of different organic remains interred in different ways, as well as the type of sediment in different parts of structures, may indicate under ecological-lithological scrutiny the time when certain tectonic movements produced topographic changes at a given place.

The Meotian bryozoan bioherms of the Kerch and Taman peninsulas (between the Black and Azov seas) may also serve as indicators of uneven sea bottoms having a tectonic origin. Bryozoans (*Membranipora lapidosa Pall.*) constructed bioherms at a definite depth of the sea bottom on slopes of anticlinal elevations (Figure 12B).

Finally, regularities in orientation of shells, for instance disjointed brachiopod and pelecypod valves with convex sides directed upward (Plate I, 2-4), the growth direction of not-overturned corals, stromatoporoids, algae, and others, tracks of crawling animals appearing generally as channels on the upper side of beds and, correspondingly, as small ridges on their lower side (Plate IX), and many other biostratinomic and paleoecological indications determine precisely the upper and lower sides of beds (Vassoevich, 1932, 1951; and others). It is essential to know this when working in regions which have been subjected to strong tectonic disturbances.

In summary, the remains of fossil animals and plants can serve not only for determination of the geological age of sediments, but they have a *multiple geological indicative value*.

CHAPTER II

Field Observations

It has been usually considered sufficient, when conducting paleontological explorations, to collect an ample amount of well-preserved fossils, and to study them subsequently in laboratories. Nowadays this procedure is insufficient, because paleoecological investigations must be carried out in the field along with collecting of fossil materials.

Field observations accompanied by collecting, and various other decumentation of what is observed, comprise the basis of paleoecological investigations. No doubt, some important observations and conclusions can be obtained also in working on any collections, even if these are mere disconnected casual findings. However, a study of such material is bound to remain without field verification, and it would be impossible to broaden the conclusions based on them without subsequent field investigations.

The best assurance of success lies in observations made in as great detail and as carefully as possible. In many cases paleoecological investigations call for reexamination of already known facts, viewing them in a more penetrating manner and from the new point of view.

The close connection between paleoecological and lithological problems demands simultaneous paleoecological and lithological study of rock sections, and it is then very important for the paleoecologist and sedimentary petrologist to set up and ponder upon as many problems as possible, multiplying them, indeed, in the course of their joint field work where they also should strive to solve them.*

*Recently the problems of lithology and methods of sedimentary petrological investigations, including field investigations, have been pursued vigorously. In Soviet literature they are expounded in textbooks by M.S. Shvetsov, L.V.

The fundamental method in the domain of paleoecology is that of comparative analysis. In the course of field studies one must constantly compare the peculiarities of one bed, including its fauna and flora, with those of another, and those of one sequence of beds with those of another (the work should always be accompanied by a written record of their similarities and differences). Reexamination, after working on others, of sections earlier studied is also recommended for comparative evaluation and for search for details which might have been missed in sections originally examined but subsequently discovered in others.

A paleoecologist should strive to take into account, as fully as possible, group composition of fauna and flora, its diversities or uniformities, quantitative relationships of various species, presence of this or that life form, normal or stunted growth of individuals, degree of development of their skeletal parts, and similar data. Combination of all these data helps to understand the nature of the medium in which the organisms lived and its influence upon them.

One of the fundamental problems for which solution should be sought in the field is whether an observed accumulation of fossilized remains represents an ancient biocoenose or an aggregate of forms which did not live together, i.e., a thanatocoenose.

The following is necessary for solution of this problem: *1*) acquaintance with dominant ecological aspects of the animal groups encountered (for instance, it would be inappropriate to include in a biocoenose containing sedentary brachiopods nektonic or planktonic tentaculites which may have been buried with them), and *2*) evaluation of the degree of influence exerted by an aquatic environment in producing a given accumulation of organic remains. Water

Pustovalov, and L. B. Rukhin, in "Metodax isucheniya osadochnykh porod" [Methods of study of sedimentary rocks], Vols. 1 and 2 (1957) and in "Spravochnom rukovodstve po petrografii osadochnykh porod" [Handbook on petrography of sedimentary rocks], Vols. 1 and 2 (1957). A very valuable manual on conditions of sedimentation is "Uchenie o fatsiyakh" [Facies science], now in its 3rd edition (1956), by D. V. Nalivkin (translated into English and available on microfilm, AGI).

In Western literature, among important books on the subject such titles should be mentioned as H. B. Milner, 1962, Sedimentary Petrography, Vol. 1, Methods in Sedimentary Petrography; Vol. 2, Principles and Applications; F. J. Pettijohn, 1957, Sedimentary Rocks; L. M. J. U. van Straaten, 1964, Deltaic and Shallow Marine Deposits.

currents capable of transporting dead bodies of animals, as well as shells and other hard parts, from one place to another, depositing them according to their volume and weight on various parts of the sea bottom, are principal factors in the origination of thanatocoenoses.

In addition to scattering the shells of bivalves, water currents affect their orientation, and the same is true of other skeletal remains and carcasses (Plate I, 2-4; Plate II). In order to appreciate the work of water and to determine whether deposited shells are autochthonous or allochthonous, much importance must be attached to perfection of the organic remains as opposed to their abraded or fragmented condition, although it is not to be overlooked that surface features of the shells of living mollusks may suffer loss in relief.

To be noted further is the fact that, especially in shallow, agitated waters, changes in local conditions of life and concomitant sedimentation may occur very quickly and as a result strata formed under these changing conditions may be very thin. An ability to differentiate evidence of these different conditions is very important. For instance, Plate V, 3, illustrates the attachment of a brachiopod on a stromatoporoid. This could have happened only after death of the latter, which apparently occurred in connection with a local change in life conditions; therefore, the stromatoporoid and *Cyrtospirifer* attached to it characterize different conditions of life and of sedimentation.

Evaluation of the character of a sediment is of paramount importance in a paleoecological analysis of faunas and floras, and in differentiating biocoenoses and thanatocoenoses. Preservation of biocoenoses intact is favored in fine-grained sediments deposited in quiet waters, but not in coarser sediments. Under favorable conditions we find some organic remains in their unaltered life position. Examples of this are known among homomyarian pelecypods, lingulids, and a few natural groups of articulate brachiopods buried in clays, marls, fine-grained limestones, and other rocks at some horizons in the Main Devonian Field of the European U.S.S.R. (Plate I, 1; Plate V, 1 and 2). Under these conditions benthonic invertebrates have been buried in various stages of growth, so that one may find shells in early stages of development associated with adult and senile shells (Plate XII, 2).

Many components of biocoenoses, even those of agitated waters, may be encountered in their place of growth, and may be represented by individuals in different stages of growth. This is explained by the occurrence in such settings of hard rocky bottoms, pebbles, or large shells, and, correspondingly, of a large number of attached forms belonging to the diverse groups of invertebrates. They were not detached from the substratum after death and were not carried away by water currents. Excellent examples are biocoenoses of abraded rocky bottoms and bottom gravels of Devonian seas on the Russian Platform, in which are found bottom-fixed brachiopods and pelecypods, auloporid and *Rugosa* corals, tubicolar worms, crinoids and thecoids (Edrioasteroids) (Plate V, 5; Plates VI and VII).

Adnate and attached marine organisms are particularly interesting because when found together they are commonly cemented to one another, so that it may not only be said that they are components of one and the same biocoenose, but also *partners in the more intimate relationships of symbiosis (mutualism or commensalism) or even of parasitism.**

Such interesting records are not particularly rare in the past: they are known from the beginning of the Paleozoic, and search for them may disclose examples in deposits of any geological age (Plate IV, 1; Plate V, 5; Figure 5). When analyzing such findings it is necessary, first of all, to ascertain whether they may not possibly be mere attachment of one kind of organism to another subsequent to the latter's death. It is obvious that any foreign organism could become attached to the inner side of a brachiopod and pelecypod valve only after death of the individuals which secreted these hard parts. Likewise, should we find an adnate coral spread over a shell (e.g., *Cyrtospirifer)*, transgressing without interruption from one valve to another, we have reason to conclude that the coral settled on the brachiopod after death of the latter or, at

---

*By mutualism or symbiosis (in a narrow sense) is understood a form of relationship between two organisms which is beneficial to both; commensalism, or food dependence, consists of a relationship in which feeding advantage is gained by only one of the two organisms; and parasitism exists where one of the two is utilized by the other as its source of food, or as a habitat, usually harmful to the host.

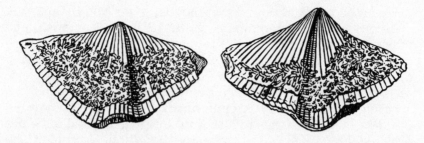

Fig. 5. Development of *Aulopora gekkeri* Chernyshev on both valves of *Cyrtospirifer schelonicus* Nal. up to its defined growth stage, marked by a sharper growth line (showing evidence of commensalism, in the course of which growth of the brachiopod became interrupted, apparently because of sickness, this being disastrous for the coral). Svinord beds of the Upper Devonian of the Main Devonian Field, Koloshka River. Natural size.

least, that spreading of the coral from one valve to the other occurred after death of the brachiopod.

The same possibilities should be remembered in interpreting various kinds of cavities in shells and other skeletons which are foreign to their own known structure. These could be: *a*) dwellings of commensals (e.g., tubes of the commensal worm *Hicetes* in the Devonian colonial coral *Pleurodictyum problematicum* Goldf., and tubes in zoaria of the Ordovician bryozoan *Diplotrypa petropolitana* Pand. (*Mesotrypa excentrica* Modzal.) (Plate IV, 7-9), as well as tubes of the commensal worm *Chaetosalpinx* in Paleozoic favositids (Figure 6); *b*) dwellings of parasites (Plate IV, 2-4, 10 and 11); *c*) tunnels of diverse organisms in shells of live invertebrates, which if not too numerous (*Palaeosabella*: Plate III, 2) do no harm to their host, but if very numerous pass to parasitism. Borings of the sponge *Cliona*, the worm *Polydora*, and the pelecypod *Lithophaga* in the oyster shells (Plate III, 4-6) illustrate such cases.

Boring organisms, such as the worms *Trypanites* and *Polydora*, and the mollusk *Lithophaga*, frequently settle on and penetrate pebbles and hard rocky sea bottoms (Plate VI, 1; Plates VII, VIII and Plate XV, 2; Fig. 31).

Tunnels, canals, and holes formed by invertebrates, channels bored by algae, and tracks of crawling animals on the surface of sedimentary layers or within them are documents of ancient life which differ fundamentally from the usual "body fossils" (that is petrified hard skeletons or secreted remains of extinct animals and plants and

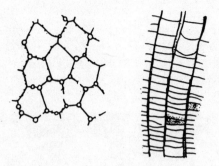

Fig. 6. Tubes of a commensal worm, *Chaeto-salpinx ferganesis* Sok., in colonial coral *Favo-sites*. Fergana Silurian. (Sokolov, 1948). X 6.

carbonized plant tissues), as well as impressions of the soft parts of animals. All such indirect organic documents are called *"life traces."* They may belong to skeleton-bearing animals, but most commonly they belong to animals lacking hard parts or certain algae. Fossils of this sort are distributed widely in deposits of the geological past and in some no other kinds occur, or they are encountered very rarely in the form of shell detritus and microfauna. Flysch deposits are characterized by predominance of "life traces" as the only evidence of organisms associated with them.

Organisms lacking hard parts now constitute a large percentage of many biocoenoses and the same is true of past time. Therefore, researches including field observations of this kind of organism is quite necessary for reconstruction of extinct biocoenoses.

Many such fossils are quite characteristic of certain facies, particularly those of shallow seas not far from strand lines and therefore are good indicators of them. They can also be used successfully for determination of the upper and lower surfaces of beds (see p. 4, and Plate IX, and Plate XI, 5).

Because the nature of these fossils long remained quite enigmatic, they were assigned to a group known as *"Problematica."* Many of them are still erroneously considered to be imprints of algae, roots of terrestrial plants, or features of inorganic origin. Thanks to paleo-ecological analysis, reinforced by wide application of the actualistic method, it has become possible to decipher the true nature of ancient fucoids and chondrites (Plate X, 2; Fig. 7), *Rhizocorallium* (Plate X, 1), *Corophioides* (Plate XI, 1 and 2), *Rhizolites* (Plate XI, 3; Plate XV, 1), *Zoophycos*, *Spirophyton* or *Taonurus* (Plate X, 3), *Helminthoides* (Plate XI, 4) and other structures.

Fig. 7. *Chondrites bollensis* Zieten, Lower Jurassic, Holzmaden, Germany (Hauff, 1953). X 0.8.

It has been determined that fucoids and chondrites comprise branching tunnels of mud-eaters, seemingly worms in friable sediment; and that specimens of *Rhizocorallium* and *Zoophycos*, *Spirophyton* or *Taonurus*, represent looped horizontal or spiral trails with an embracing tunnel also made by mud-eaters, probably worms. *Corophioides* and *Rhizolites* are pocketlike, looplike, or simple burrows of decapod crustaceans or other animals, which are disposed vertically or obliquely to the surface of beds. *Helminthoides* form looplike passageways parallel to and touching each other on the sea bottom, apparently produced by worms.

Other tracks and borings are left by crawling or burrowing mollusks and other animals. However, many "Problematica" still await explanation (e.g., *Caulerpites*, Plate XI, 5). Therefore, these fossils demand particular attention both in the field and in subsequent investigations.

Traces of vertebrates which generally are easier to recognize than those of invertebrates may be found as fossils. In the U.S.S.R. few traces of vertebrates have yet been found but footprints of Late Cretaceous dinosaurs (Plate XIV, 1), Miocene birds, artiodactyls, and predatory mammals have been discovered.

A thorough study of fossil organic remains reveals some peculiarities to which little attention has been given in the past, and which have not been systematically studied. At the same time these varied "life traces" (in a broad sense) allow deeper penetration into the problems of organic life of the geological past, and of its medium (see the good compilation of these problems by Abel, 1935). Among peculiarities of this kind are the following:

1) *Features of paleotaxiology* (Richter, 1955), which relates to the behavior of extinct animals. Figures 4 and 5 provide examples and additional illustrations of the co-existence of animals or interrelationships among organisms which can be seen in Plates III-V, likewise illustrations of life traces in Plates VIII-XI.

2) *Pathological phenomena and marks of mechanical injuries which occurred during the life of an organism* (domain of *paleopathology*). An example given in Fig. 8 shows the broken rostrum of a belemnite with rejuvenation of its growth, and Plate IV, 5 and 6, illustrates shells of ammonites and brachiopods with healed traces of bites by some predators; not infrequently encountered are fractures with the broken parts grown together again and pathological swellings in the bones of the vertebrates.

3) *Phenomena of reproduction and early growth stages.* Examples are fossil fishes with contained roe (Plate XII, 1), eggs of dinosaurs and birds, and embryos of ichthyosaurs within the body of an adult female, and of juvenile trilobites, brachiopods, ammonites (Plate XII, 2 and 3), and other organisms.

4) *Facts from the domain of nutrition and feeding.* Here belong the canal mouths and tubes of worms, and colonies of auloporid corals located along the anterior margin of brachiopod valves (Plate III, 2; Plate V, 5; Fig. 5); the worms and corals settled along this edge because they were assured of a supply of food and oxygen, and during the continued growth of the brachiopod shell the auloporids and worms (*Serpula*) followed advance of the anterior edge of the valves; circular holes bored by predatory mollusks [gastropods] (Plate III, 1) are encountered in the shells of

Fig. 8. Longitudinally sectioned rostrum of *Cylindroteuthis absoluta*
(Fisch.), revealing rostral injury
during early growth. Lower Volga
stage of Upper Jurassic, Volga River
at Ul'yanovsk city. X1.3.

brachiopods and pelecypods; attachment of the gastropod
Platyceras above the anal vent of crinoids (Plate IV, 1); discoveries inside the body of adult ichthyosaurs of young ichthyosaurs which had been swallowed; remains of plants between the teeth and in the stomach of carcasses of mammoths
and woolly rhinoceroses; tooth marks of predators on bones;
coprolites (excrements) of various invertebrates (Fig. 9)
and vertebrates, and excreta of birds and other animals.

5) Molted skeletal parts of trilobites (Plate XIII, 2),
ostracodes, and higher crustaceans.

Paleoecologists should remember that many components of ancient faunas and floras could have left no evidence
of their presence because of their lack of hard structures
durable enough for preservation as fossils.

We can study these extinct organisms only from traces
which they have left behind, such as trails, borings,
coprolites, accumulations of organic matter and the like.
At the same time we may broaden our concepts of the

Fig. 9. Tubes of burrowing animal filled by excrements (coprolites) of marine invertebrates (worms or mollusks). Podol'sk horizon of Middle Carboniferous, Onega River. (Khvorova, 1953). X 15.

contents of populations belonging to this or that biotope, considering in a general way the food-gathering problem of organisms which subsequently were fossilized or which left other evidence of their existence. In certain rare cases impressions of entirely soft-bodied animals are found (for instance, jellyfishes, worms, and a few others), or impressions of the soft bodies of animals with an internal skeleton (e.g., belemnites from Solnhofen, ichthyosaurs

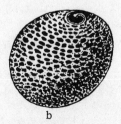

a   b

Fig. 10. Color ornament preserved in fossil shells. a-*Theodoxus rarizonatus* Gabunia. X 6; b- *T. liliae* Gabunia, Middle Miocene, Georgia. (Gabuniya, 1950). X 10.

from Holzmaden) which were preserved under some special conditions of burial. Among very rare fossil remains are bird feathers from the vicinity of Lake Issyk-Kul in the Kirghiz S.S.R. (Plate XIII, 4), and ink sacs of dibranchiate cephalopods from the bituminous shales of Jurassic age in the Volga River region (Plate XIII, 1). Plate XIII, 3, shows a cavity formed by a spider caught in the resin of amber. In very exceptional cases even the color pattern of a shell is preserved (Fig. 10). Structures formed on the sea bottom by reef-building organisms (that is, *bioherms* and *true reefs*) have special interest in paleoecology. Facies favorable for making such structures have always existed in seas of the geologic past but in the course of geologic time different groups of reef-building organisms have succeeded one another. Such were algae, foraminifera, sponges, archaeocyathids, stromatoporoids, hydroids, various coral assemblages, and bryozoans.

Owing to favorable living conditions in these biotopes (high temperature, great water agitation, good illumination, abundance of food and oxygen), they were inhabited also by numerous representatives of other animal groups, the hard parts and solid secretions of which contributed to growth of the reef structures.

Geologists and paleontologists initiated study of bioherms and reefs much later than study of ordinary layered rocks. Consequently, a vast and very interesting task remains for the future in studying bioherms and reefs of diverse geological ages. Such fossil reefs are abundant in the Ordovician and Silurian of North America, in the Silurian of the British-Baltic area, and in a broad Devonian reef belt which extends from northern North America through central Europe, Urals, central and southeastern Asia to Australia. In the U.S.S.R. they have been encountered and studied in deposits of Cambrian, Permian, and Neogene ages (Figs. 11 and 12).

The appearance of reef bodies in geological sections frequently has created difficulties for stratigraphers who segregated them in special stratigraphic horizons without considering the possibility of rapid lateral transition into stratified formations. The study of the reefs is of particular practical interest. For instance, the discovered subsurface Permian reefs in the region of the "Second Baku" have proved to be great reservoirs of petroleum.

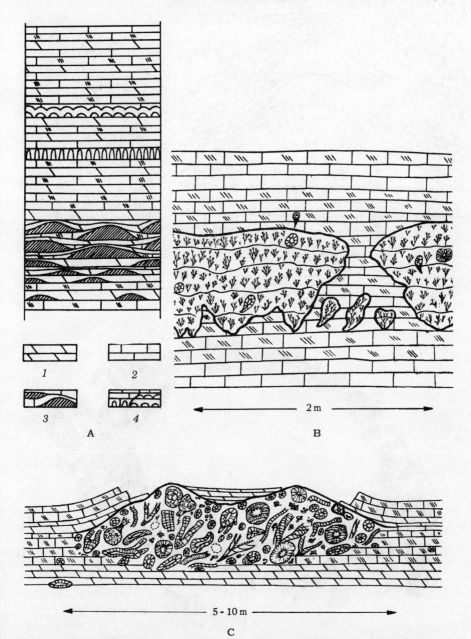

Fig. 11. Lower Cambrian bioherms on Lena River, Yakutsk region, Siberia.
A. Diagrammatic section of variegated series, 1:1500 (1-shaly dolomitic limestone; 2-slightly shaly dolomitic limestone; 3-archaeocyathid bioherm; 4-algal bioherm). B. Algal bioherm. C. Archaeocyathid bioherm. (Zhuravleva and Zelenov, 1950).

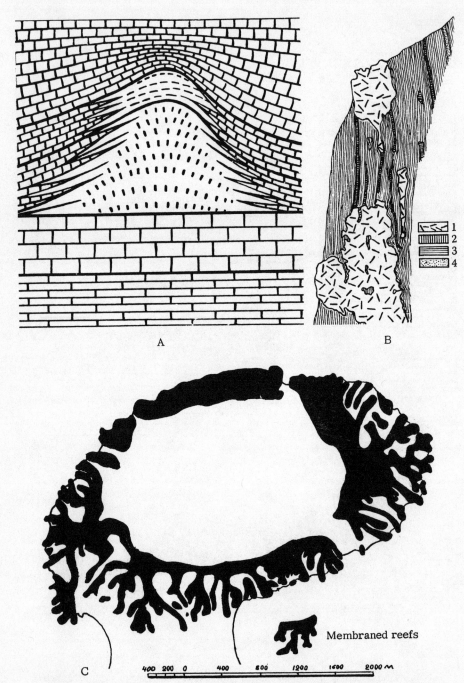

Fig. 12. Lower Permian and Neogene bioherms. A. Lower Permian bioherm near Kungur, Cis-Urals. B. Neogene (Meotian) bioherm of Kerch Peninsula, Crimea. 1-Membranipore bioherm; 2-detrital beds with membranipores; 3-clays; 4-volcanic ash. (After Kolesnikov et al., 1940). C. Distribution of the membranipore bioherms surrounding anticlinal elevation in the bottom of Meotic sea, Kazantip Point, Crimea. (Andrusov, 1909-1912).

CHAPTER III

Field Collecting

Collection of material for paleoecological studies should illustrate field observations as completely as possible.

Further, the collected specimens should be sufficient to provide for laboratory analyses and for documenting various paleoecological problems. It is important to bear in mind also the need to collect materials suitable for paleoecological exhibits and for exchange of duplicates in order to obtain comparative documentary and exhibit material.

Above all, search in the field should aim at careful collecting of specimens particularly valuable from paleoecological and lithological points of view. Gathering of as many fossils as possible, recommended in paleontological instructions, is equally desirable for our purposes because they help in finding specimens of paleoecological value. Mass material is needed also for determining variability of forms, discovering injuries inflicted during the life of organisms, establishing intimate biocoenotic relationships between different forms, and judging degree of preservation of fossils.

In view of need not only to collect paleontological remains but also to determine their placement in the fossil-bearing beds (that is, their occurrence in this or that sedimentary layer and in relation to its parts, their orientation, and so on), a survey of the section should precede the collecting of fossils. After bed-by-bed study of a section, accompanied by measurements, sketches, and descriptions, many loose fossils in rubble may be allocated more or less precisely to a bed or group of beds, and occasionally even their proper orientation within them. Accordingly, it is recommended that before proceeding with study of a section one should make preliminary examination of the outcrop and of the rubble. Since the supply of fossils found on the surface and especially on the rock face of a section is by no means unlimited, premature extraction prior to a detailed study of an exposure entails loss of a substantial part of their value as paleontological documents, just as a fossil removed from rock matrix without noting its orientation and other particulars of its occurrence loses a large part of its value.

It is necessary to indicate on fossil-bearing fragments detached from rock beds, and/or on fossils themselves, the original top and bottom surfaces (as by inscribing the letters *t* and *b*) with a suitable crayon. The same indications should be marked with a pencil or sharp tool on lithologic samples. It is also necessary to record the orientation of elongate shells relative to cardinal directions (N, S, E, W) if the orientation is generally repetitive.

It is desirable to collect the most characteristic specimens (sometimes even weathered ones, if these reveal some important details), and, in removing them from surrounding rock, to protect their surface from accidental damage by hammer blows. The specimens should also be protected from rubbing, scratching, and breaking during transportation, which can be prevented by suitable tight packing. For the purpose of exhibiting assemblages of fossils it is desirable to collect some loose sediment to serve as background in mounting the fossils, and also to gather fragments of hard rocks for filling gaps between edges of fossil-bearing slabs that do not exactly fit together.

Fossil collecting should be supplemented by a quantitative evaluation of the fauna (flora) encountered in a bed and on its different surfaces. It is necessary to count number of species and to evaluate degree of abundance of each in the observed fauna (flora), accompanied by an indication of growth stages, degree of preservation, etc. Relative frequency may be marked by numerals of a grade system, but it is better to express this by such words as "many," "few," "dominant," "rare," "isolated individuals," or in some more precise fashion. It is recommended also in working on fossils in unconsolidated rocks to count their number directly by unit squares of a surface, such as 25×25 cm or 50×50

cm, or better, if faunal composition is homogeneous in depth, to count numbers by unit volumes.

In the literature (Ivanova, 1946b) one may find description of the method of designating estimated relative abundance of species encountered in a fauna (flora) by abbreviated Latin words: *soc* (*sociales*) — where a fossil, by its great abundance in an exposure of a given horizon or bed, creates a sort of biological background; *cop* (*copiosae*) — where a fossile is abundant, but not in every exposure; *spar* (*sparsae*) — where a fossile is encountered as isolated individuals in almost every exposure; *sol* (*solitariae*) — where a fossil is encountered only in rare exposures; and *uni* (*unicum*) — where a fossil is encountered in very small number in a single exposure.

The collecting of a fauna and flora should not be limited to fossils freed from rock matrix and separated from each other. For the paleoecologist most significant fossils are those preserved in adhering rock, because such specimens show direct connection of the fossil organism with its habitat, or characterize conditions of its burial. Of great interest also are the occasionally preserved life groups. In view of this, it is desirable to collect both isolated specimens of a fauna and flora and, most essentially, entire groups contained in a rock.

Particularly interesting are the bedding surfaces with sorted out and regularly oriented fossils, with some fossils overgrowing others, some with holes of boring organisms, and other evidences of organic action on the sea bottom, or the surfaces of layered beds with evidence of action of physical forces (with ripple marks, evidences of erosion, and so on). Such peculiarities may be observed best in large specimens with a haphazard outline. Likewise, it is not desirable to restrict lithological samples to any special size and form, such as formerly standarized petrographic specimens: they become thereby insufficiently demonstrative and besides, their artificial uniformity is unattractive.

Therefore, for characterizing fossil sediments it is desirable to collect not only the series of the ordinary fragments — including chips for slides and analyses — that should not be too large, because generally they would not be placed in museum displays, but also some slabs of naturally acquired size and form. Such slabs of comparatively large size, and also some extra-large slabs and blocks, best display the peculiarities which are desirable to illustrate by natural specimens (for instance, "fossil sea bottom" with its inhabitants, other surfaces noticeable for their peculiarities, and others). Expositional value of large specimens is particularly great, whereas the cost of transporting them is comparatively small; furthermore, their weight may be reduced considerably by trimming, especially if only one of their surfaces is important; or they may be collected as separate pieces which later may be joined together.

CHAPTER IV

Preparation of Materials

Collected paleoecological materials, as well as ordinary paleontological and lithological specimens, should be utilized to the maximum possible extent in working out theoretical and practical problems of biology and geology.

The preparation of paleoecological materials in the laboratory should be integrated with field observations and together should lead to a greater insight into problems encountered.

Analysis of specimens should be as detailed and diversified as possible, and because of this it is desirable to make comprehensive use of comparative materials, including data derived from observations of living animals and plants.

A paleoecologist should endeavor to reveal as fully as possible the interrelationships of various animals and plants with one another and with their inorganic environment. If he is unable to obtain unequivocal answers to all questions he should not be discouraged, since such relationships even of some living organisms are yet unknown.

Just as in field work, the laboratory stage of an investigation should combine paleoecological and paleontological observations, with accompanying study of the lithology of the rocks, and full evaluation of other geological data. Such many-sided working out of the data becomes possible when specialists in several scientific disciplines cooperate with each other. We should always seek to widen the scope of the research and to augment, correspondingly, the collective work of specialists engaged in the study of the paleoecological material. Whenever, in the course of ordinary paleontological investigations, paleospecialists on particular groups of fossil organisms limit themselves to study of only their selected organisms, paying little attention to others, it may become necessary for complete paleoecological investigations to arrange for the study of remaining groups of organisms. It is necessary to clarify the paleoecological peculiarities of the representatives of all these groups separately, and of the whole complex of forms jointly.

At the present time, however, hardly a single fossil fauna or flora has been studied so fully and many-sidedly; because of this a paleoecologist is obliged to organize a study of whatever is left out in work on the systematics and phyletics of various faunas and floras to which paleontologists have previously paid insufficient attention. When studying these groups of organisms anew, paleoecological demands should be taken into account. The same demands should be applied also to those groups of organisms which were previously worked out only from a morphological-systematic point of view; now they should be restudied with inclusion of their paleoecological aspects.

In organizing such additional studies it is usually revealed that groups of organisms which are richest in occurrence have been studied most completely, partly because they are most important stratigraphically or partly because they are the best preserved. Groups which most frequently have been neglected are poorly preserved or they comprise numerically insignificant forms, or they are represented by mere "life traces." However, such "*small groups*" and life traces of invertebrates are of considerable paleoecological interest, for they augment substantially our concepts of the form complexes which existed together, and numerically insignificant forms also may illuminate their own life conditions as well as those of the whole complex to which they belonged.

Paleoecologically important also are organisms which could be expected but actually are lacking in a given complex, in which event the reason for their absence needs to be explored.

The history of exploration of the Fergana Paleogene fauna has demonstrated the value of these approaches. Of this fauna only the excellently preserved oysters were completely described at first. Other pelecypods and the gastropods were very incompletely studied systematically, partly because of their poor preservation. The holes of burrowing invertebrates encountered in the rocks of almost all horizons, and frequently in large numbers (Plate XV, 1), have not been correctly understood and commonly encountered claws of decapods have been almost unmentioned in the literature. Likewise, no proper evaluation as indicators of life conditions in the Fergana Bay was given to the rare occurrence of sea urchins and barnacles, and to the absence of nummulitids, brachiopods, and cephalopods.

The absence of the last-mentioned three groups of invertebrates, the rare occurrence and small size of discovered sea urchins, and the extreme rarity and small size of hexacorals (which were also discovered in the course of detailed paleoecological investigations of the Fergana Paleogene) came to be recognized as indicators of an abnormal salinity of the water in the Fergana basin at different times in its history.

The importance of studying "life traces" has been emphasized. The investigation of a particular kind of previously unnoticed boring organism found in the Fergana Paleogene deposits (Plate XV, 1) has indicated that they were exclusively shallow-water forms, and study of claws observed in every exposure has proved that they belong to decapod crustaceans of the genus *Callianassa* which made the mentioned borings. At present *Callianassa* lives in the littoral zone and in shallower parts of the sublittoral. This evidence permitted using occurrences of *Callianassa* borings in sediments as indicators of the proximity of shore lines of the Fergana Bay in the Paleogene sea of Central Asia.

Preservation of the remains of any particular group of organisms may be so poor as to preclude identification of them at a specific level and to prevent establishment of trustworthy new species. It is very desirable, of course, to know the exact systematic position of fossil forms, but inability for mentioned reasons to determine this exactly is not calamitous from a paleoecological point of view. This is because specific classification providing names of fossils as a rule explains nothing of the ecology (unless the forms are still living or very close to organisms still living, the ecological status of which is well established). More important than exact taxonomy is a morphofunctional analysis of a fossil remnant. In such

cases, therefore, a paleoecologist must be content with
identification of a fossil to its generic rank, and occasionally he may be satisfied with establishment of still higher
systematic rank.

This is illustrated, for instance, by poorly preserved
groups of mollusks in the Fergana fauna, whose ecological analysis has given most valuable results.

Internal and external molds of pelecypod and gastropod shells assigned to the genera *Meretrix, Diplodonta,*
and *Eulima* have shown by their small size and gregarious
character of the few species that there was a general
impoverishment and stunting of the Fergana Bay fauna
at certain moments of its existence, whereas the mass
occurrences of the inner and outer molds of *Unio* shells
have proved a considerable reduction of the salinity of
its waters at these times (Fig. 21B).

Already mentioned is observation that in order to
clarify the mode of life of extinct organisms it is necessary to study their skeletal remains and life traces more
profoundly — both kinds being equally important. Therefore, it is desirable in the course of laboratory investigations to conduct, first of all, a detailed morphofunctional analysis of fossil remains, and then to study
the skeletal remains to determine different kinds of vari-
ables: individual, ontogenetic, ecological, geographical —
so as to detect evolutionary changes in the course of time.
The results of these investigations should be carefully
integrated with lithological data, and also with other geological data, with a view to finding out what kind of connection may exist, firstly, between them, and secondly,
with those changes which have taken place in their life
medium. It is also important to find out whether these
changes occurred in a single group of organisms only,
or in several groups simultaneously, and so on.

The working out of ecological problems in given paleontological materials should be pursued along *two different,* and yet *intimately connected, approaches.* One is
autoecological, and the other *synecological.* Under autoecological approach (autoecology) is meant a study of only
one chosen systematic group of organisms of greater or
less volume, or even of only its chosen representatives,
whereas under synecology is meant a study of the ecology
of the whole organic complexes or biocoenoses.

Such subdivision and distribution of work is natural, because its total normally exceeds the ability of any one person.

Autoecological investigations belong to early stages of a complete paleoecological analysis, being necessary prerequisites for a subsequent synecological analysis and a synthesis. As examples of works containing autoecological chapters may be cited papers by Maksimova (1955) on Middle and Upper Devonian trilobites, and by Makridin (1952) on Upper Jurassic brachiopods. A paleontologist who specializes in a particular group of organisms, and who at the same time should be a paleoecologist for this group, ought to integrate his work with that of a paleo-synecologist, who preferably should be an expert in one of the groups. A synecologist conducts his field work in company with a lithologist and it would be desirable, although not obligatory, that specialists in all other groups would join them. A synecologist shares his observations, materials, and conclusions with other paleontologists, and either alone or together with them, he integrates all the material and derives from it his synecological conclusions. An example of this is work by Ivanova and Khvorova on the fauna of the Middle and the Upper Carboniferous of the Moscow basin.

Summation of the results of paleoautoecological investigations devoted to a separate group of organisms in a fauna or flora is not a substitute for a special paleo-synecological investigation or a special paleosynecological monograph on a given biota in its totality, in which the whole population of a studied fossil basin should be considered. Likewise, the population of a certain basin or land sector as a biotic complex with all its ramified inner relationships and concrete biocoenoses needs to be studied, all this in intimate connection with life conditions in their historical aspect. A paleoecological study of a given group of organisms or of a complex of fossil forms begins with a study of their mode of life and their ecological relationships in a small sector of geological time. After elucidation of all that may be possible for this moment of geological history, one may attempt a further delineation of characters and changes in ecological relationships in the course of time beyond this moment. In such ways one passes from a "static paleoecology" to a "dynamic paleoecology": to establishment of successive changes in ecological relationships in time, that is, to establishment on the one hand of ecological changes in a given systematic group and on the other hand to establishment of the evolution of the biocoenoses and of the general ecogenesis of the organic world of a given ancient basin or part of an ancient land. Likewise, we should not attempt to investigate at once a large territory, but rather enlarge an area of investigation gradually.

In a properly organized field and laboratory investigation we seek to determine the ecology and ecological rules which existed in the life of populations of greater or less size, and of greater or less geological duration, whether distributed in large parts of an open sea or in partly closed marine basins, bays, or lakes, and correspondingly of greater or less land areas, for a substantial duration of their geological existence. Examples of such investigations are already mentioned works by Ivanova and Khvorova on the fauna of the median and late Carboniferous sea of the Russian Platform, studies by Gekker on the Late Devonian fauna of the Main Devonian Field, by Gekker et al. (1963) on the Paleogene population of the Fergana Bay of Central Asia and others. These and other investigations have made apparent a number of general regularities applicable to ancient organic life and sedimentation.

Comparison of various results of autoecological investigations of separate systematic faunal (floral) groups and ensuing results of synecological investigations of paleobiocoenoses and complete biotas of various basins located in tectonically different regions* and of different geological ages will permit some generalized paleoecological and evolutionary conclusions and through them bring out broader ecological and evolutionary regularities.

Because of the very intimate relationship between ecology and organic evolution one cannot expect to understand the evolution of complexes of organic forms without understanding ecological peculiarities of the separate constituent forms and their life conditions. Besides, without this knowledge the origin of species and subspecies

*Basins of the platforms, of the geosynclines, foremountain sags, intermountain depressions.

and evolutionary events of separate groups of organisms can be only recorded, not always correctly, but frequently they *cannot be explained*. It follows that it is imperative to regard the phylogenetic development of various groups of organisms in the light of their dependence on physico-geographic and biotic factors of the life medium, and changes in the latter in the course of geological history of a given group.

Such should be the present requests addressed to paleontologists who study separate groups of fossil organisms. But such requests may be fulfilled by them only *in cooperation with synecologists* who are called on to elucidate the contents and ecological peculiarities of the whole complex of organic forms and in cooperation with lithologists to determine conditions of the environment in which the complex lived, making use of all paleontological and geological data for solution of this problem.

Following is the order of questions which a contemporary paleontologist may formulate when studying a paleontological object. In this same order, from easier to increasingly more difficult, was the sequence of the problems which confronted paleontologists at successive stages in development of the science of paleontology. In connection with this new divisions of paleontology have arisen and begun to develop one after another.

A. Questions regarding paleontological *remains*:
1) *What* is it and its name?—Systematics.
2) *When*?—Stratigraphic position.
B. Questions regarding fossil *organisms*:
3) *What was the function* of separate organs?—Functional morphology.
4) *How did they live?*
5) *Where did they live?* } Paleoecology.
General conclusions: ecological regularities.
6) *How have they changed* in
time and space?
7) *Why have they thus changed?* } Problems of evolution.
General conclusions: evolutionary laws.

This table shows that the first two questions when asked during early stages in the development of paleontology usually were considered by paleontologists only in terms of fossils as petrified remains of once-living organisms. But questions 3-7 are concerned with the

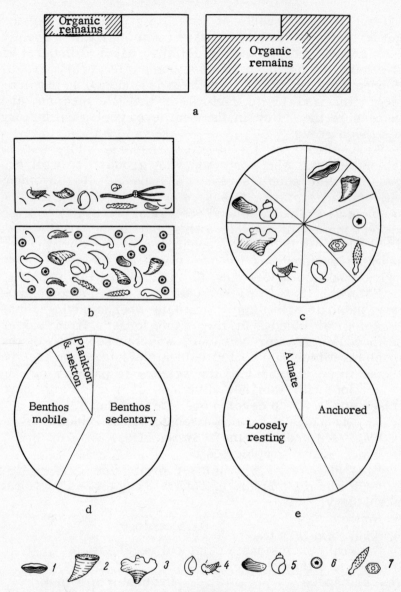

Fig. 13. Diagram showing paleoecological analysis of facies of near-shore shallow-water zone in Middle and Upper Carboniferous of the Moscow basin. a-Density of organic remains in limestone beds (left) and in marl and clay beds (right). b-Character of burial of organic remains in marl and clay beds (above) and in limestone beds (below). c-Systematic composition of organic remains. d-General ecologic classification of organic remains. e-Ecologic classification of brachiopods. Symbols for kinds of organisms: 1-foraminifers; 2-solitary tetracorals; 3-bryozoans; 4-brachiopods; 5-gastropods and pelecypods; 6-crinoids; 7-echinoids. (Ivanova, 1949b).

extinct organisms themselves and manifest the beginning of a new, progressive stage in the development of paleontology. Questions 4 and 5 are strictly paleoecological, and are intimately connected with question 3, functional morphology. Profound paleoecological investigations lead to the formulation of ecological laws. Questions 6 and 7 are evolutionary ones in a narrow sense of the word, being connected intimately with ecological questions (4 and 5), and a response to question 7 is generally inconceivable without a profound paleoecological analysis of the fossil organisms. The ultimate goal of the formulated set of questions on evolutionary paleontology (in a broad sense) is recognition of evolutionary regularities closely related to ecological ecological regularities.

The possibility of utilizing paleoecological and biostratinomical data for stratigraphic purposes, with employment of new methods for more detailed stratigraphic subdivision of the sediments, has been explained in Chapter 1. Also briefly discussed there was the direction along which these data should be worked out for solving the current problems in lithology, facies, paleogeography, tectonics, and genesis of some useful minerals. It should be remembered that the more elaborate the paleoecological analysis undertaken the more exact will be the stratigraphical and other geological conclusions obtained. Figure 13 shows a graphic method for illustrating results of a paleoecological analysis of populations in a given facies, as suggested by E. A. Ivanova (1949b). Such a scheme provides information on density of fossils in a rock, their mode of burial, and also the systematic and ecologic nature of the fauna and flora.

CHAPTER V

Graphic Illustrations

In this chapter are recorded various methods of graphic representations of paleoecological (as well as lithological and facieological) data and generalizations. Preparation of such illustrations constitutes an obligatory part of work for a paleoecologist. Profiles, maps, and various diagrams serve not only for illustrating and generalizing pertinent features, but construction of them is regarded as a method of demonstrating regularities in the relationships of facies and their change, of organisms and their migrations, etc.

Generally speaking, graphic methods should be employed as much as possible since they are more effective and precise than expression of observations and thoughts by words, and in the field they are faster. Sketches are good substitutes for lengthy descriptions and in the field they permit reduction of notes to a few words, or mere letters, arrows, etc., added to sketches.

1. FIELD SKETCHES

Most widely used in paleoecological field practice are schematic sketches and somewhat more exact line drawings. Whenever feasible the use of colors is also desirable. Schematic sketches are usually employed for illustrating geological sections. These may be drawn in the form of columns bounded on one or both sides by straight vertical lines, or, in a manner better suited to our purpose, in the form of steps which depict the observed natural profile of an exposure of interbedded hard and soft strata, the resistant beds forming benches and the weak beds making slopes or reentrants (right side of Fig. 14). The relief effects of differential weathering

62

can be added also to the columnar sections by outlining more resistant beds by heavier lines or by extending them laterally farther than less resistant beds, as is done frequently by American stratigraphers and paleontologists.

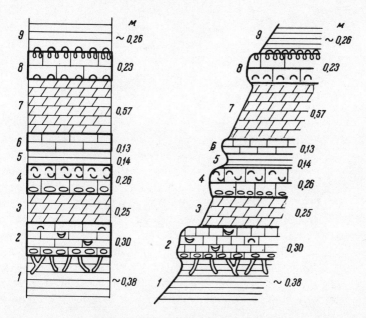

Fig. 14. Two different ways of drawing diagrammatic columnar sections.

Conventional symbols for various types of rocks and their texture (crossbedding, surfaces of weathering), either worked out by an author himself or taken from field geology textbooks, should be used in all sketches uniformly. The position of fossils in a bed should be indicated also (near the base, in the middle or upper part or at a contact of beds); also concentrations of fossils, their orientation, nature of preservation (e.g., separate or joined valves of pelecypods and brachiopods), holes of burrowing animals, tracks of crawlers, and others.

In describing exposures, these sketches preferably should be placed in the field notebook in such way that sufficient space is left on a side for bed-by-bed description, and for listing of faunistic (floristic) contents, frequency of the occurrence of this or that species, etc. In view of this it is most convenient to place the sketch on

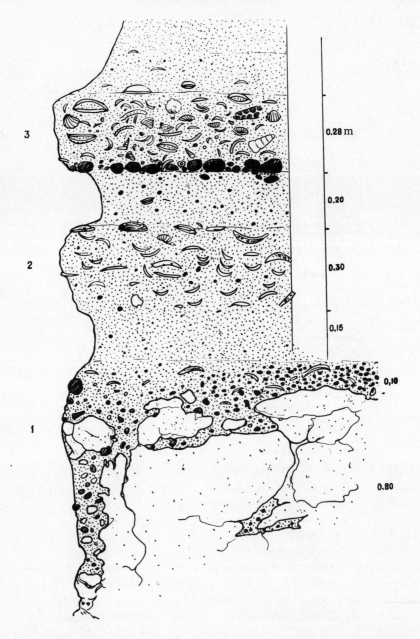

Fig. 15. Sketch of outcrop showing structural and textural peculiarities of rocks, distribution of molluscan shells, degree of abundance, preservation, and orientation. Basal part of Suzak stage in northern Fergana, Varzyk (field sketch).

the left page of an open notebook. The selected scale should be sufficient for showing in the sketch all observed details.

In order to make sketches which approach natural appearance as closely as possible, one can draw them in the fieldbook — and for a subsequent use in publication — in more informal manner, as illustrated by Figs. 15 and 16. In this kind of sketch the symbols to indicate the lithology are not drawn with a ruler and a triangle, but

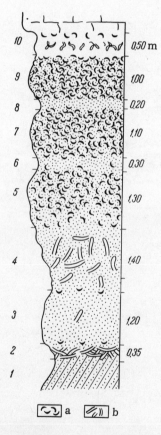

Fig. 16. Sketch of section showing oyster beds composed of *a*) separated valves of *Ostrea (Turkostrea) turkestanensis* Rom., variously oriented, and *b*) burrows of decapod crustacean *Callianassa*, Alai stage of Paleogene, southwestern Fergana, Sulyukta (field sketch).

in a freehand, somewhat schematic, fashion, showing an actual development of cleavage in a rock, actual distribution in it of faunal and floral remains, and other peculiarities.

When in the field it is important to sketch all kinds of observed details: disposition and orientation of fossils, peculiarities of their burial, any peculiar structural details, special developments pertaining to surfaces of individual beds, etc. (Figs. 17 and 18). In some cases a studied object needs to be sketched in several views.

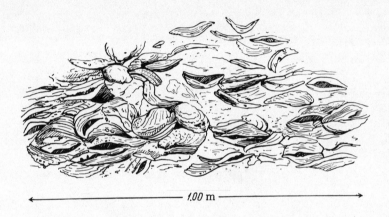

← —————————— 1.00 m ——————————→

Fig. 17. Oyster bank built by *Ostrea hemiglobosa* var. *kafirniganica* Burač, Suzak stage, northern Fergana, Aksai (field sketch).

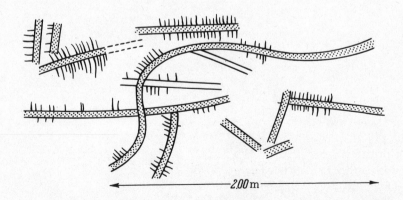

← —————————— 2.00 m ——————————→

Fig. 18. Stigmaria with attached rhizoids, on upper surface of clayey limestone, Lower Carboniferous, on Retisha River northwestern part of Moscow basin (field sketch).

The scale of sketched objects should be supplied, and in the case of similarly oriented objects (crests of ripples, lengths of shells, plants, and other fossils, and others), also their position in relation to points of the compass. The sketches should be simple line drawings, with simplified shading when objects are convex, with emphasis on all important peculiarities, and omission of unimportant features.

It may be desirable to sketch separately some particularly interesting or illustrative parts of an exposure, or of peculiarities in the stratification of beds, etc. For this same purpose water colors or crayons may be used especially for showing some important colors of rocks (for instance of mottled rocks).

Pencil sketches are made by medium hard grade of a graphite pencil; and when a sketch is made of subjects in perspective, the use of two or three pencils of different hardness is suggested, drawing nearest subjects with the softest pencil, next farther ones by a harder pencil, and features farthest away by the hardest (Fig. 19A). In this simple way an effective perspective can be achieved easily. Coloring of various geological horizons and layers is preferably on tracing paper placed over a sketch rather than on the sketch itself and the colors preferably should be as close as possible to natural colors of the rocks. Figure 19B is an example of such geological treatment of a geological landscape by symbolic hachures on a tracing paper overlay covering the sketch shown in Fig. 19A.

2. SKETCHES FOR PUBLICATION

Line drawings made in the field, when inked in, provide very desirable illustrative material for both publications and museum displays.

The schematic sketches of cross sections should be supplied with conventional symbols which indicate various systematic fossil groups, such as genera, and even species (Fig. 20). For the purpose of easier reading these symbols should approach in a simplified way the contours of the fossils which they indicate. They should be drawn exactly opposite the beds in which the fossil was found. Relative

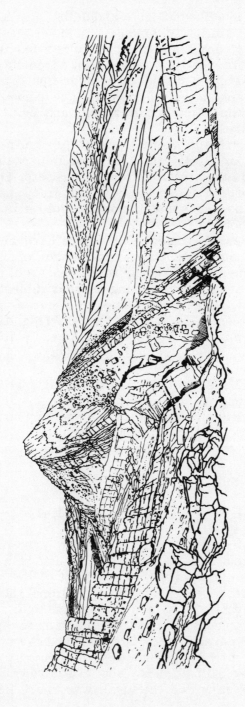

Fig. 19A. Cross section of Paleogene, Surkha locality, east of Varzyk village in northwestern Fergana. (Field sketch made with pencils of different hardness.)

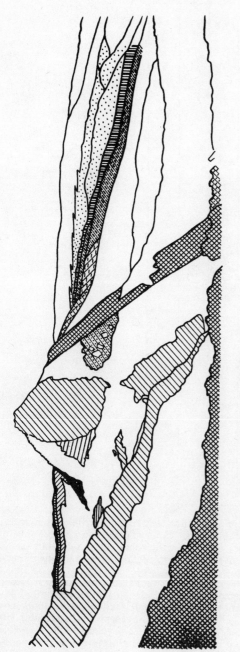

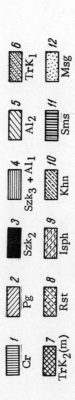

Fig. 19B. Stratigraphic indications for Fig. 19A expressed by patterns or by crayons, on tracing paper superposed over the sketch. 1–Cretaceous; 2–Paleogene, undifferentiated, Subdivisions of marine Paleogene; 3–middle Suzak horizon; 4–upper Suzak and lower Alai horizon; 5–upper Alai horizon; 6–lower Turkestan horizon; 7–middle Turkestan horizon; 8–Rishtan stage; 9–Isfarin stage; 10–Khanabad stage; 11–Sumsar stage; 12–Massaget stage (continental uppermost upper Paleogene and continental Neogene).

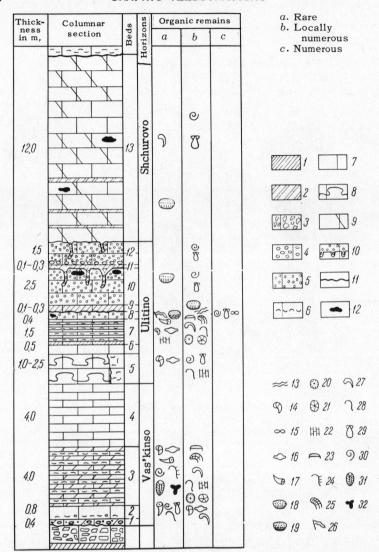

Fig. 20. Diagrammatic sketch of columnar section, with symbols indicating occurrence of various animals and plants in different strata.
Legend: 1-clays; 2-ferruginous clays; 3-calcareous breccia; 4-limestone conglomerates; 5-coprolitic limestones; 6-microlaminated and ooze limestones, with interlaminated organic detritus; 7-micro-oolitic and ooze limestones; 8-algal biostromic limestones; 9-dolomitized limestones; 10-deep animal burrows at bases of coprolite intercalations; 11-disconformity; 12-siliceous concretions; 13-stromatolites; 14-small foraminifers; 15-paleonubecularids; 16-fusulinids; 17-solitary *Rugosa* corals; 18-chaetetids; 19-colonial *Rugosa* corals; 20-crinoids; 21-echinoids; 22-bryozoans; 23-*Chonetes*; 24-*Linoproductus*; 25-*Dictyoclostus*; 26-*Meekella*; 27-*Choristites*; 28-undetermined brachiopods; 29-pelecypods; 30-gastropods; 31-trilobites; 32-fish remains (Ivanova and Khvorova, 1955).

abundance of various fossils may be shown by a difference in the size of the respective symbols, or in some other way. When such symbols are added to a cross section the symbols which indicate rock-building organic remains should be retained inside the cross sections.

The separate cross sections may be then combined into the general sections, or the schemes of distribution of the fauna and flora (with a great exaggeration of the vertical scale over the horizontal, but keeping relative distances between the combined sections).

There should be at least *three* kinds of such paleoecologic *profiles* or *diagrams*: *1) stratigraphic, 2) lithologic* or *sedimentary profile*, and *3) general paleoecological sections*.

In a stratigraphic profile only the stratigraphic subdivisions are shown by color or hachures.

In a general lithologic profile the separate beds or layers of rocks are shown within the stratigraphic subdivisions. Any diagenetic changes should be detected in the course of a lithological study of the rocks, and the restored original appearance of the sediments should be shown and so mentioned. Then such a profile may be called a sedimentary profile (Fig. 21A). The composition of the rocks or sediments is indicated in the profile by hachures or by color as close to their characteristic natural color as possible.

For paleoecologic profiles stratigraphic profiles are used, to which are added boundaries of beds. Symbols may be used to depict the faunas and floras belonging to the beds (Fig. 21B). The various species, genera or larger systematic groups (or the various complexes of forms and biocoenoses) can be so indicated. Typical symbols include circles, dots, crosses, straight lines, variously inclined lines, and schematic outlines of the fossils. Furthermore, for an indication of forms or groups of forms (for instance, inhabitants of the near-shore zone, of a zone farther away from shore, and so on; or euryhaline, stenohaline, and others (Fig. 23); or burrowing, adnate, crawling, and so on), the contour symbols are filled with dots or solid ink. Different frequencies of the occurrence in different parts of a profile may be indicated by corresponding differences in the number of their symbols, or by the differences in their size.

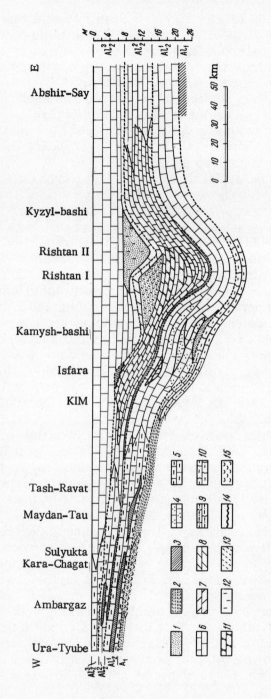

Fig. 21A. General section showing distribution of late Alai sediments in southern part of Fergana Bay. (Sedimentary section.)

Legend: 1–sands; 2–silts; 3–gray and green clayey ooze; 4–sandy calcareous ooze; 5–clayey calcareous and clayey detrital ooze; 6–detrital, coquinoid, and oyster–bearing sediments; 7–calcitic dolomitic ooze; 8–dolomitic ooze; 9–calcareous silty ooze; 10–calcareous clayey ooze; 11–dolomitized calcareous sediments; 12–calcareous cement; 13–dolomitic cement; 14–irregular surface of erosion; 15–oyster banks (after Osipova, 1956).

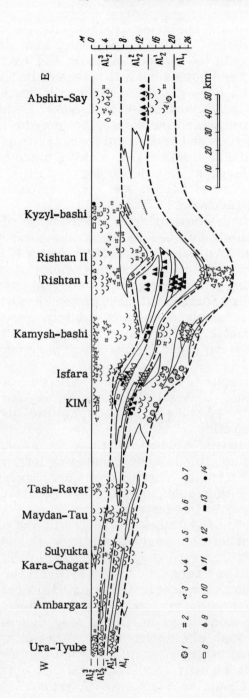

Fig. 21B. Schematic distribution of late Alai fauna and flora in southern part of Fergana Bay. (Paleoecological profile).

Legend: 1–echinoids; 2–bryozoans; 3–serpulids; 4–oysters; 5–Turritella; 6–Meretrix; 7–Cardita; 8–Panopaea; 9–Cardium; 10–Cucullaea; 11–Eulima; 12–Meretrix tschangirtaschensis; 13–Unio; 14–Diplodonta aff. renulata. Solidly inked symbols indicate inhabitants of waters with reduced salinity. (After Osipova, 1956).

When working out and analyzing a paleoecologic section
it must be realized that benthonic, nektonic, and planktonic organisms could be buried together, and that the
benthos could have been buried not in the place of its habit.
This latter situation does not count when making small-
scale profiles (or maps and other diagrams), because,
as a rule, the dead bodies and skeletons of bottom-dwellers
are not shifted by waves and bottom currents far from the
place where they lived. However, in making more complete or localized large-scale paleoecologic profiles (see
below) the coincidence of habitat and place of burial or
lack of it should be recorded.

The profiles which show together distribution of the
sediments, organisms contained in them, and their ecological peculiarities are called *facieologic profiles*. Such
profiles show particularly clearly the dependence of various bottom forms and particular groups of organisms associated with various sediments (that is in the cases where
they are buried at the place of their habitat). Here are
given some additional remarks concerning the construction of profiles showing faunal, floral, and sedimentary
distribution:

1) If the stratigraphy is simple (the profile embracing
only a few horizons) it is possible to omit any special
stratigraphic profile, because a stratigraphic background
is given in other profiles.

2) Intervals between studied sections in a profile
may be left blank or filled in by connecting interpola-
tions, which is preferable. This can be done, however,
only when evidence for such interpolation is adequate.
In describing a profile the factual material used for it
should be mentioned and by lines on the profile the place
and vertical extent of the studied sections should be
indicated.

3) If facies of the sediments are very variable and
in vertical succession show frequently repeated alternation
of beds of different lithology and organic content, the
profiles may be schematized in such a way that within
separate horizons such alternation of the different types
of rocks and corresponding organic assemblages may be
shown by a smaller number of alternations than actually
present, but this should be mentioned in explanation of
the profile.

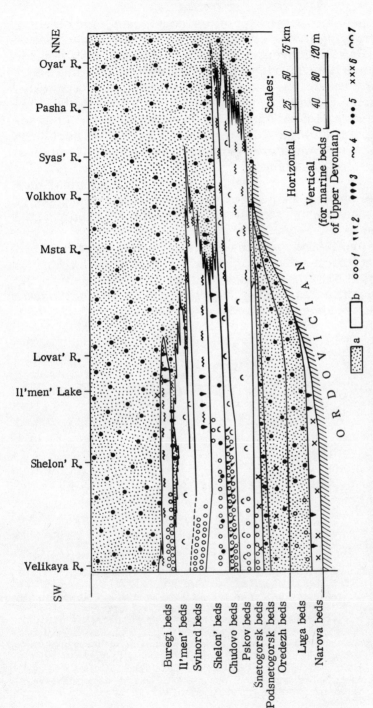

Fig. 22. Partial paleoecological profile of Middle and Upper Devonian in eastern half of the Main Devonian Field.

Legend: a–lower red beds, upper variegated beds, and near-shore marine sands; b–marine and lagoonal deposits; 1.stromatoporoid and blue-green algae (Girvanella–Pycnostroma); 2–Rugosa; 3–Lingula; 4–worm tubes; 5–fishes other than Osteolepis, Dipterus, and Ptyctodus; 6–Osteolepis and Dipterus; 7–Ptyctodus.

4) In paleoecologic profiles constructed for strata of highly varying facies or extremely rich in fossil remains, a crowding of conventional symbols makes it difficult to distinguish the distribution of different forms and separate groups of organisms. As remedy, it is suggested that supplementary profiles should be added to the complete ones, each of the added profiles showing only selected paleoecological information (Fig. 22). In such profiles certain groups of organisms or other paleoecological peculiarities are shown.

5) For the same reason some paleoecological data may be shown, as already mentioned, on tracing paper superposed on a profile showing distribution of the sediments.

The profiles become insufficiently demonstrative where change of facies is very gradual, extending through great horizontal distances. In such cases it is desirable to add to the profiles of facies diagrams showing *zonal distribution of the sedimentary facies and biota* (Fig. 23). Such

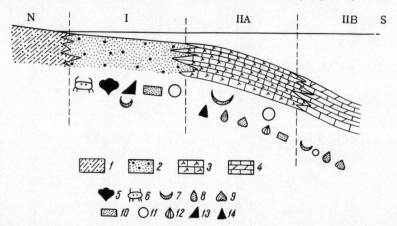

Fig. 23. Diagram showing distribution of sediments, fauna, and flora in zones and facies; median Suzak epoch (Paleogene). Northern part of Fergana Bay (see map Fig. 29).

Legend: I–littoral zone; IIA–upper part of shallow zone; IIB–lower part of shallow zone; 1–deltaic red beds; 2–gravels, sands, and terrigenous calcareous deposits; 3–detrital, oolitic, and foraminiferal calcareous deposits, oyster banks, coquina; 4–fine-grained calcareous, dolomitic calcareous, and silty calcareous ooze; 5–calcareous algae; 6–burrowing crustacean *Callianassa*; 7–oysters; 8– *Meretrix*; 9–*Cardita*; 10–*Panopaea*; 11–*Pectunculus*; 12–*Cardium*; 13–*Potamides*; 14–*Eulima* sp. Horizontal line indicates sea level. Symbolic indications of euryhaline forms are filled with dots, and those of inhabitants of waters with reduced salinity filled with ink.

diagrams help to clarify regularities in distribution of the sediments and organic forms and their complexes on the bottom of an ancient basin with indication of their natural succession (in units designated "gammas," "rows," and "chains").

Such sketches may be given (whenever possible) indicating a band of changing sedimentary deposits between the shore line and depths of a basin, with conventional symbols for animals and plants indicated above each "link" of the sedimentary "chain" so as to indicate populations in parts of the bottom. The band indicating organic forms may be made of two rows, an upper one indicating the more abundant or prevailing forms by large symbols and a lower row marking by smaller symbols organisms which play a secondary role. Such diagrams are composed for small divisions of geological time, and wherever sufficient factual data are available for the particular parts of a basin in which the situation may be different.

In addition to the mentioned graphic illustrations of paleoecological and sedimentary data and generalizations, other schemes may be invented.

For instance, the diagram shown in Fig. 24 shows *distribution according to depths of the fauna and flora* at successive ages in the history of a basin.

A comparison of such successive diagrams should show *1)* some organisms clearly restricted to certain determined zones; *2)* occasional shifting in their distribution within the zones, for which an explanation should be sought; and *3)* some changes which have taken place in the basin population and its zonal distribution at the times of general transformations of life conditions (for instance, in the salinity of water).

Diagrams showing stratigraphic distribution of particular organisms, where these are shown by one color, or by a single conventional symbol, with organisms listed in systematic order, merely indicate an appearance of some forms (or groups of forms), disappearance of others, outbursts in their developments or periods of diminution—but they do not reveal any ecological peculiarities and life conditions of the faunas and their constituent organisms. Such diagrams serve to raise questions regarding the existence of some kind of physicogeographical processes leading to the observed changes in the organic world. But

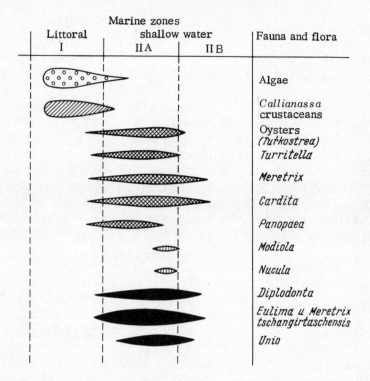

Fig. 24. Diagram of zonal distribution of basic megafauna and flora of Fergana Bay, median late Alai.
Legend: Crosshatched pattern – euryhaline forms; vertical hachure – inhabitants of waters with normal salinity; solid black – inhabitants of brackish waters; IIA. upper part of shallow-water zone; IIB. lower part of shallow-water zone.

wherever organisms are grouped together in a diagram on the basis of some ecological character—such as tolerance to a particular salinity (as shown in Fig. 25)— they indicate *1*) just what united some organisms together and *2*) what kinds of changes in salinity in the basin have taken place in the course of time.

Of greater demonstrative value are combined *diagrams of stratigraphic and facieological distribution* (Fig. 26) which are accompanied by a columnar section representing lithology. The succession of rocks shown in the column provides a definite (though of course incomplete) indication of certain events in the physicogeographic life of a basin, events which not only influenced an outburst or diminution of one group of organic forms or another but

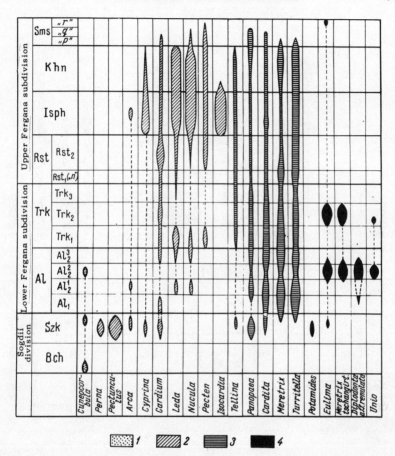

Fig. 25. Diagram of stratigraphic distribution of some genera and species of pelecypods and gastropods in Paleogene of Fergana.
Legend: 1-inhabitants of strongly saline waters; 2-inhabitants of normal saline waters; 3-euryhaline forms; 4-inhabitants of brackish waters.

represented dynamic factors that caused changes and evolution of the faunas and floras, induced their migration, or led to annihilation of part of the basin's population.

Similar to the diagram given in Fig. 26 is one showing *phylogeny and facies-belonging* of various species of a given genus, and within the phylogenetic branches of which are indicated the species and lithologic facies in which they are encountered (Fig. 27).

Most interesting and instructive are so-called *"syngenetic diagrams"* introduced by Kolesnikov (1949), in which is shown a particularly designed phyletic tree for

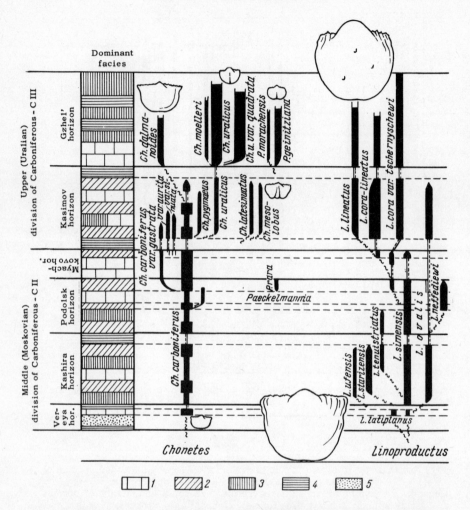

Fig. 26. Diagram of stratigraphic and facieologial distribution of *Chonetes* and *Linoproductus* species in Middle and Upper Carboniferous deposits, southern part of the Moscow basin.

Legend: 1-limestone; 2-marl; 3-dolomite; 4-clay; 5-sand. The thickness of the line indicates the number of frequencies of the evolving forms.

a group of animals, for instance of a family of mollusks, and side by side are placed one or several distribution maps (Fig. 28). The phyletic tree is designed against the background of successive zones of the sea bottom, and in it relationships between the different species are clearly projected, as well as the extent and zonation of their distribution. Small maps show the arrangement and migration of various species. Such diagrams depicting

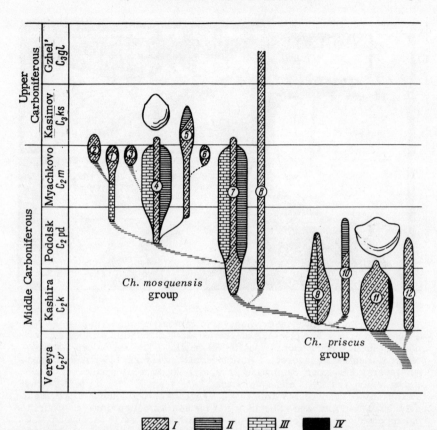

Fig. 27. Diagram of phylogeny and facies relationships of two groups of
Choristites Fisch. (groups of *C. mosquensis* and *C. priscus*) in Middle and
Upper Carboniferous, Moscow basin.
Legend: I–interstratified clays and limestones; II–bioclastic limestones; III–
ooze limestones; IV–dolomites (after Ivanova, 1949b). 1–*Choristites loczyi*
Frcks em. Chao; 2–*Ch. loczyi* Frcks em. Chao var. *transversalis* A.&E. Ivan.;
3–*Ch. tashenkensis* A.&E. Ivan.; 4–*Ch. mosquensis* Fisch.; 5–*Ch. mosquensis*
Fisch. var. *solida* A.&E. Ivan.; 6–*Ch. mosquensis* Fisch. var. *lomgiuscula*
A.&E. Ivan.; 7–*Ch. sowerbyi* Fisch.; 8–*Ch. densicostatus* Ivan.; 9– *Ch. radi-
culosus* A.&E. Ivan.; 10–*Ch. n. ex.*; 11–*Ch. priscus* Eichw.; 12–*Ch. uralicus*
Leb. var. *brevicula* A.&E. Ivan.

the sequence of events in time and space portray the fates
of various systematic organic groups.

Wherever available materials are sufficient for illumination of more than one direction in space (that is more
than one "line profile"), but also of a certain area, then to
the various mentioned profiles are added *lithological maps*
or *sedimentological, paleoecological,* and *facieological*

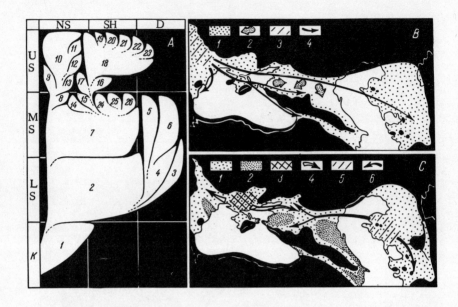

Fig. 28. Syngenetic diagram of Sarmatian *Mactridae*.
A. Diagram of stratigraphic and paleobathymetric distribution of species. Legend: NS–shallow near-shore deposits; SH–shallow deposits; D–deep-water deposits; K–Konkskian layers; LS–lower Sarmatian layers; MS–middle Sarmatian layers; US–upper Sarmatian layers; 1–26, various species of *Mactra* (among which are 2–*M. eichwaldi* Lask.; 7–*M. fabreana* d'Orb.; 8–*M. pallasi* (Baily); 15–*M. subvitaliana* Koles.) B. Diagram of distribution of species in early Sarmatian time and at beginning of median Sarmatian time. Legend: 1–regions populated by *M. eichwaldi* Lask.; 2–invasion of early Sarmatian *Mactra* into deep-water zone; 3–region of original development of *M. fabreana* d'Orb.; 4–migration paths of this species. C. Diagram showing migrations of middle Sarmatian *Mactra*. Legend: 1–regions inhabited by *M. fabreana* d'Orb.; 2–regions inhabited by deep-water *Mactra*; 3–region of original development of *M. subvitaliana* Koles; 4–migration of paths of this species; 5–region of original development of *M. pallasi* (Baily); 6–migration paths of this species; (after Kolesnikov, 1949).

maps for successive ages in the history of a basin, which correspond to determined stratigraphic horizons or to their subdivisions. In lithological maps the distribution of rocks (by zones, or in greater detail) is shown; in sedimentological maps, the distribution of the original sediments; in paleoecological maps, the distribution of various fossil organisms or of their groups. The facieological maps (Fig. 29) synthesize our knowledge of the distribution and interrelationships of the sediments and inhabitants of a basin to the limits of a studied area. The symbols and colors in maps are the same as in profiles.

Just as in the case of making profiles, it may be recommended, when material is overly abundant, to draw the paleoecological data on superposed tracing paper. In comparison with maps entered in "syngenetic diagrams" (Fig. 28), such maps are advantageous in showing *1*) the substrata and *2*) the complexes of the forms which inhabited the basin.

As paleoecological investigations continue to develop one new type of graphical illustration after another

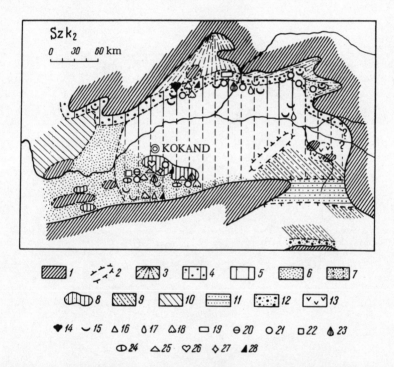

Fig. 29. Diagrammatic facies map of Fergana Bay in Paleogene (middle Suzaksky stage).

Legend: 1-land; 2-shoals; 3-red deltaic deposits. Marine deposits: 4-sandy calcareous deposits with pebbles and gravelly sands with burrows of crustacean *Callianassa*, and algal calcareous structures; 5-foraminiferal, detrital, and oyster-bearing calcareous deposits (dotted lines indicate inferred distribution); 6-sands and silts, locally with pebbles and burrows of *Callianassa*; 7-sands and silts, sporadically carbonaceous, locally with pebbles and burrows of *Callianassa*; 8-terrigenous dolomitic and dolomitic oozes; 9-clayey and silty clayey oozes; 10-clayey and diatomaceous oozes; 11-coarse terrigenous deposits; 12-sands with pebbles. Lagoonal deposits: 13-gypsum; 14-calcareous algae; 15-oysters; 16-*Turritella*; 17- *Meretrix*; 18-*Cardita*; 19-*Panopaea*; 20-*Lucina*; 21-*Pectunculus*; 22-*Cyprina*; 23- *Cardium*; 24-*Cucullaea*; 25- *Arca*; 26-*Modiola jeremeijevi*; 27-*Cuneocorbula*; 28- *Potamides*.

continues to appear, each major work almost inevitably introducing some kind of novelty in the way of illustration. Thus, Figs. 2, 3, 13, 20-27, 29, and 30 are borrowed from various works of a paleoecological nature accomplished in the Paleontological Institute of the Academy of Sciences of the U.S.S.R.

Very informative are *"diagrams of distribution"* of a species, showing together pathways of dispersion and times of migration (Fig. 30).

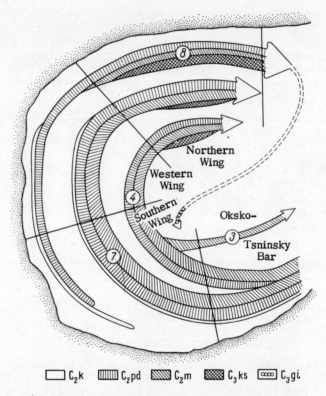

$\square \, C_2k$ $\text{⫿⫿⫿} \, C_2pd$ $\text{⧄⧄} \, C_2m$ $\text{▨} \, C_3ks$ $\text{⊂⊃} \, C_3gi$

Fig. 30. Diagram showing distribution of *Choristites mosquensis* Fisch. group in the Moscow basin. Different horizons of Middle and Upper Carboniferous indicated by conventional patterns.
Legend: 3–*Choristites tashenkensits* A. and E. Ivan.; 4–*C. mosquensis* Fisch.; 7–*C. sowerbyi* Fisch.; 8–*C. densicostatus* Ivan. (Ivanova, 1949b).

Much may be accomplished by a tabular statement of relationships between paleoecologic observations and conclusions (illustrated by Table 3 as an example. In one column numerous observations may be listed concerning the deposits of a basin, their organic content of indigenous plant and animal life associated with organisms carried to sites of sedimentation from surrounding areas, peculiarities of burial of the organic remains, and like features. In another column all seemingly trustworthy conclusions derived from study of the separate observations and groups of them can be recorded similarly. Comparison of the two columns with the object of correlating the maximum possible number of items in each with the other should lead to generalizations having great value. The correlation may be indicated graphically by drawing lines which join observations and pertinent conclusions, crisscrossing one another complexly (as was done by Gekker) or by numbers and letters which provide cross-references constructed for this English version because judged to be simpler and clearer (Table 3).

One of the ultimate goals of a paleoecological investigation should be as complete as possible "reconstruction" of life with all its aspects of various organisms out of faunal or floral complexes in the course of their existence.

Such "reconstructions of life of the geological past" should be given in the form of written essays, but these should be also illustrated by "life pictures" (the previous name for them was "geological landscapes": Plate XVII). A paleoecologist should start thinking of such "life pictures" and should begin to collect material for them at the very beginning of his investigations.

The "life pictures" should be given separately for each natural complex of forms (biocoenosis), for each facies, and for each geological time interval; one should avoid the so-called "menagerie-pictures," where on a single sheet of paper is shown in an unnatural assemblage the whole or greater part of a known fauna (flora) of a given interval of geological time.

Table 3. CORRELATION OF OBSERVATIONS AND CONCLUSIONS

[Observations (numbered) are cross-indexed

OBSERVATIONS

I DEPOSITS OF KARA-TAU BASIN AND THEIR CONTENT

(1) Outcrop belt of Jurassic "fish shales." Breadth not great (B′)
(2) General section of Jurassic, thickness great (F, G)
(3) Disturbances of normal stratification (G)
(4) Tectonically caused limitation of Jurassic belt (F, G)
(5) Jurassic basin shores formed by Paleozoic rocks (J, K)
(6) Sandstones and conglomerates interbedded with "fish shales" (I, P, Z)
(7) "Fish shales" interbedded with very fine-grained, laminated, calcitic and dolomitic beds containing small pyritic concretions and much organic matter but no primary gypsum (A, N, Q, U, V, C′, I′, L′)
(8) Admixture of terrigenous clay particles and sand grains with inter-layers of sandy silt (O)
(9) Interlayers composed of Paleozoic limestone pebbles with evidence of subaqueous flows and slides (F, G, H, K, Y)
(10) Ripplemarks (rare) (J′)
(11) Desiccation cracks (rare) (J, M, J′)
(12) Traces of subaqueous slides (F, G, H, Y)
(13) Syngenetic pebbles of carbonate ooze and fish scales (J, M, W, J′)
(14) Absence of salts (chlorides, sulfates) (A′)
(15) Bedding surfaces of "fish shales" with fragmentary plant and animal remains (O′, P′)
(16) Bedding surfaces with accumulations of less fragmentary plant re-mains or moderately complete individual animals (M′)

II ORGANIC POPULATIONS OF KARA-TAU BASIN

Fishes [See Insects (below), food sources for fishes; and Flying Reptiles, for which fishes furnish food]
Numbers of species and specimens:
(17) Numerical relationshipa between different species (H′)
(18) Particular species of fish predominating in local occurrences (H′)
(19) Abundance of fish remains (G′)
Peculiarities and regularities of preservation:
(20) Fishes excellently preserved (X, L′)
(21) Presence of young fishes and fish with roe (X)
(22) Fishes split in two halves (W)
(23) Fishes usually large and many buried together (M′)
(24) Localized occurrence of fish accumulations, abundant in some places but absent in others (H′, M′)
(25) Quantitative relationships of variously bent fish carcasses lying on their sides, and character of bending (J′, O′)
(26) Bent fish carcasses with lower or upper side of head resting on bed-ding plane (W, J′, O′)
(27) Decomposed carcasses of fishes found at places of their burial (very rare) (P′)
(28) Accumulations of fish carcasses with varying degrees of common orientation, including some piled in ripple bands (M, J′, M′, N′)
(29) Fish scales in ripple bands (along ripples) and pebbles of consoli-dated ooze with fish scales (P′)

Turtles
(30) Presence of fresh-water forms (B′)

RELATING TO THE JURASSIC KARA-TAU LAKE AND ITS ENVIRONS
to deductions (lettered and vice versa)]

DEDUCTIONS

I CLIMATE

(A) Subtropical, arid around lake (7, 37, 38, 45, 46)
(B) Humid in mountains (49, 50)
(C) Winds and ascending air currents present (agencies for transport of plant remains and insects into Kara-Tau basin) (43, 53)
(D) Mixing and dispersal of air-borne materials (43, 44, 51, 53)
(E) Basinward water drift caused by wind (locali zed and temporary) (52)

II DISPOSITION OF KARA-TAU BASIN AND NATURE OF SHORES OF LAKE

(F) Mountainous surroundings (2, 4, 9, 12)
(G) Location of lake in narrow tectonic depression elongated in NE-SW direction (2, 3, 4, 9, 12)
(H) Seismicity of region (?) (9, 12)
(I) Composition of rocks along shores of lake (6)
(J) Proximity to shore of burial places of terrestrial animals and plants (5,11, 13, 39, 40, 54)
(K) Presence of elevated, locally steep and rocky shores covered by forests (5, 9, 38, 40)
(L) Weak development of low shores, swampy areas far from Kara-Tau lake shores (46, 47)
(M) Presence of some soft muddy (ooze) shores (11, 13, 28, 52)

III REGIMEN OF RIVERS

(N) River waters periodically discharged into lake (7)
(O) Terrigenous materials transported and discharged by rivers (8)
(P) Deltaic deposits formed along shores (6)
(Q) Ca and Mg salts dissolved in river waters (7)
(R) Organic remains carried by rivers: plants, pieces of wood (40, 42)
(S) Transportation of hydrophilic forms from distant places (47, 48)
(T) Insects, both adults and pupas of Diptera?, carried by rivers (57)

IV CARBONATE DEPOSITS OF KARA-TAU BASIN

(U) Noneolian, chemical or biochemical origin of carbonate ooze (7)
(V) Quiet conditions of carbonate ooze deposition and its periodicity (7)
(W) Viscous, sticky nature of carbonate ooze (13, 22, 26, 52)
(X) Suitability of ooze for promoting petrification processes (20, 21, 40, 52)
(Y) Susceptibility of ooze to subaqueous sliding (9, 12)
(Z) Local change of carbonate ooze to sand and gravel toward shores (6)

V WATER REGIMEN OF KARA-TAU BASIN

(A′) Not a marine gulf (14, 31)
(B′) But large lake (1, 30, 33)
(C′) With very hard water, rich in dissolved Ca and Mg (7, 32, 34, 36, 56)
(D′) Waters clear, not turbid (33)
(E′) Salinity in parts of basin unfavorable for some aquatic animals (34, 36, 56)
(F′) Paucity of aquatic vegetation (35, 47)
(G′) Richness in fishes (19)
(H′) Varied conditions of life and burial in different parts of basin and their changes in same place with lapse of time (17, 18, 24, 55)
(I′) Seasonal life of lake associated with periodicity of water influx and evaporation (7)

OBSERVATIONS (continued)

Branchiopods (Estheria)
(31) Presence of branchiopods (A′)
(32) Branchiopods very small, comparatively rare (C′)

Gastropods
(33) Generic composition (B′, D′)
(34) Diminutive size (C′, E′)
(35) Scanty occurrence (F′)

Pelecypods
(36) Absence (C′, E′)

[*Aquatic vegetation* (not encountered)]

III LAND PLANTS AND ANIMALS

Terrestrial flora (forest vegetation dominant)

General nature of flora:
(37) Composition of plant groups (A)
(38) Xeromorphic aspect of forms (A, K)
(39) Number of species (large) and quantity of remains (large) (J, K)

Peculiarities of preservation and burial:
(40) Preservation good or excellent, many remains including large parts of plants (J, K, L, R, X, L′, M′)
(41) Parts selectively preserved (e.g., leaves of *Ptilophyllum cutchense*) (P′)
(42) Remains consisting of pieces of wood and leafless branches (R)
(43) Presence of seeds with devices (wings) for dispersal by winds (C, D)
(44) Plant remains widely scattered or (less commonly) concentrated (D, G′)

Swamp flora (generally impoverished)
(45) Composition of plant groups (A)
(46) Hydromorphic aspect of forms (A, L)
(47) Number of species (small) and quantity of remains (small) (L, S, F′)
(48) Remains customarily fragmented (S, P′)

Insects [See *Fishes* (above), for which they furnish food]

With terrestrial life cycle:
(49) Composition of terrestrial forms by groups (very rich, including new Jurassic orders) (B)
(50) Number of species (very large) (B)
(51) Abundance of remains (large) (D, J′)
(52) Preservation variable, excellent in many (E, M, W, X, L′)
(53) Accumulations (cicadas, very rare) (J)
(54) Presence of remains on surfaces of particular beds and interlayers (H′)

With aquatic life cycle:
(55) Dragonflies (adults rare, larvae not found); May flies (*Ephemeridae*); but no remains of caddis flies (*Trichoptera*), either adults or larvae (C′, E′)
(56) Some *Diptera* present, pupas of *Tendipedoidea* (T)

Flying Reptiles [See *Fishes* (above), sources of food] [See *Insects* (above), sources of food]

DEDUCTIONS (continued)

(J′) Comparative shallowness of basin, with occasional drying of near-shore belt effected by evaporation and water draft by winds (10, 11, 13, 25, 26, 28, 51)

(K′) Erosion by waves of mud-constructed shores (13)

(L′) Comparatively quiet regime of basin (7, 20, 40, 52)

(M′) Wave work in shallow-water areas of carbonate ooze deposition, with accumulation and sorting of sediment (16, 23, 24, 28, 40)

(N′) Orientation of sedimentary structures by work of waves (28)

(O′) Deformation of deposits by wave work (25, 26)

(P′) Destruction or fragmentation by waves (15, 27, 29, 41, 48)

(Q′) Horizontal shifting of water layers with consequent dispersal of plants and insects trapped in basin (44, 53)

CHAPTER VI

Photographic Documentation
of Field Observations

Photographic documentation of field observations has a place in our work because not all investigators are able to make sketches with desirable exactitude and verity. Photography takes less time than sketching, and, finally, a photograph will always be a more truthful, though not always a more understandable, document than a sketch.

Greatest attention in the course of paleoecological investigations should be directed to photographing details, such as most interesting parts of geological sections, disclosed by the exposure, the manner of burial of fossils, the character of bed surfaces covered with animal tracks, natural fossil biocoenoses, etc. (Plates XIV, XV, XVI. It should be remembered that a photograph gives good results only when the relief of a photographed object is sufficiently emphasized by shadows; therefore objects lacking relief preferably should be sketched.

Paleoecological details should be photographed in such a way that things which need to be shown are made conspicuous and at close range photographs of desired objects (fossils and others) are focused along their whole length, as well as their background. It is advantageous, under such circumstances, to make a small, but sharply focused, photograph from a greater distance, enlarging this subsequently.

When a situation calls for focusing on frosted glass of objects occurring on a horizontal or oblique surface, where use of a tripod is impossible, photographing has to be done by holding the camera with hands. In order to be assured that focusing on frosted glass has not been lost subsequently, it is necessary to memorize the place of the camera's shadow at the time of focusing and to watch for the shadow to fall in the same place.

Each photographing of part or of an exposure should be accompanied by a schematic sketch in a notebook of what is photographed. Such a sketch should include position of individual fossils, rock boundaries with rocks indicated by number, etc.; and here should be registered also the sizes of photographed objects.

It is suggested that paleoecological subjects should not be photographed with a hammer or other foreign object used to serve as a scale. Such photograph should help a person to visualize the environment in which an extinct organism lived and the conditions under which local sedimentation occurred; a foreign object detracts from needed concentration on such matters. It is suggested instead to measure the objects about to be photographed, which will make it possible to indicate true magnification in photographic prints.

CHAPTER VII

Paleoecological Exhibits*

A paleoecological exhibit differs quite substantially from an ordinary museum display of paleontological materials. The former may be considered really good only if, in the first place, it is capable of making a museum visitor feel like entering into the field where the material was collected; secondly—and this is most important—if it is capable of creating a vision of the life conditions where the exhibited fossils actually lived; and, thirdly, if it introduces a visitor to the range of different problems pertaining to the past of our planet and connecting this past with the present.

In order to achieve this, an exhibit should be organized in a way to provide a visitor with the easiest possible comprehension of conditions in which the exhibited fossilized remnants of ancient life have been collected, and further, of restored environments wherein they lived; therefore, anything which lacks direct relationship to the outlined theme should be eliminated. For instance, desired concentration of attention may be disturbed by excessive brightness of the background on which exhibits are mounted, or by overly elaborate explanatory lettering, or even by such trifles as catalog numbers and other markings painted or stamped on the face of exhibited specimens.

Such indications (which may be permissible in collections of index fossils) are quite out of place in paleoecological exhibits, because they are out of tune with its

*It should be realized that work on paleoecological expositions may properly be considered as one of the methods of exploration. In the course of arranging a museum exhibit designed to present gathered materials vividly and in preparing an ultimately brief explanatory text and graphic sketches we begin to see the shortcomings and omissions in a not quite fully worked out problem, and this helps us to determine what needs to be done in future work.

theme and purpose, which is to show the life of geological past epochs. A simple expediency in the situation is to put inventory numerals on the lower or lateral edges of specimens.

Paleoecological exhibits can be organized desirably according to the following directions:

1) show basic ecological peculiarities in the population of different types of basins;

2) show the whole known life and its conditions in ancient basins studied in all their details, with analysis of its population in each contemporaneous facies and establishment of changes in the population through the whole time of the basin's existence;

3) show various adaptations (to different modes and conditions of life) of the representatives of a particular systematic group;

4) show the phenomena of parallelism and convergence in the representatives of one and the same group, or in different groups of organisms; conceivably also expositions of still other ecological themes.

The whole arrangement of an exhibit must be more or less unorthodox, and not conformable to the usually followed manner of exhibiting paleontological material (in systematic or geochronological order). Exhibited specimens are not lined up in horizontal or vertical rows, but are grouped in every situation differently, now closer together and now farther from each other, depending on thematical connections and the amount of the accompanying descriptive and graphical material. Rock specimens intermingle with particular fossils and with larger fossil-bearing slabs depending on a particular concept. When the available fauna and flora are prolific there is no need to exhibit all forms, but only those which are most picturesque in their characterization of particular complexes pertaining to some definite parts of an ancient water basin, and also those pertaining to particular biocoenoses; preference in an exhibit should be given to specimens (and also to slabs and large blocks) in which the fossils are preserved in place; contemporary animals and plants may be included in an exhibit to draw a parallel between ancient and living "life forms;" and so on.

The whole exhibit should be richly filled with sketches, photographs, profiles, diagrams, and reconstructions, accompanied by general statements and detailed explanations to separate objects; these should differ much from the ordinary labels. Dioramas of "ancient life" are also desirable (Plate XVII).

Generally speaking, exhibits devoted to particular paleoecological themes (especially those dedicated to some particular ancient basins) should approach the state of a vivid tale, with proof of authenticity in the form of all kinds of documentation.

In general development of the museum operation devoted to paleoecological exhibits we should keep in mind the possibility, and even necessity, to create some *"natural paleontological (paleoecological) museums,"* that is, protected natural monuments and preserves, with some general paleontological or specific paleoecological value or interest (Varsanof'eva and Gekker, 1951). Such, in the U.S.S.R., are the Kara-Tau preserve in southern Kazakhstan (Plate XIV, 2), and a natural monument with dinosaur tracks on Sataplia hill near Kutais (Plate XIV, 1). Among the smaller examples of paleoecological monuments are:

1) a part of rocky shore of the Paleogene sea with "rock-living" oysters and passages of the rock-boring mollusks near Ura-Tyube town in Tadzhik S.S.R. (Plate XV, 2; Fig. 31);

2) a layer with well-preserved holes of decapods, also in the Paleogene of Isfara River in Fergana (Plate XV, 1).

For *paleoecological monuments* should be selected those natural exposures which are of paleoecological interest, and which are also rare and may be easily defaced or destroyed by breaking off of specimens, and which in their natural surroundings are more valuable and demonstrative than they could be when transferred to a museum.

They can be found and selected in almost any country of the world.

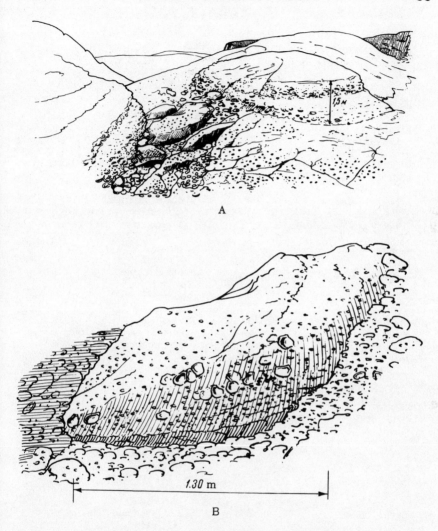

A

B

Fig. 31. Paleoecological monument (field sketches).
A. Exposure of Paleozoic limestones, riddled by Paleogene rock-boring mollusk *Lithophaga* and covered by oyster crust, which includes riddled calcareous pebbles (Alai stage of Paleogene), Tadzhik S.S.R. south of Ura-Tyube town. B. Limestone boulder encrusted by oyster *Ostrea (Turkostrea) turkestanensis* Rom. and riddled by borings of *Lithophaga* (detail).

Appendix 1

Early Pleistocene
Tertiary
  Pliocene
    Late Plioc.
    Medial Plioc.
    Early Plioc.
  Miocene
    Late Mioc.
    Medial Mioc.

    Early and Med. Mioc.
  Oligocene
  Eocene
  Paleocene
Cretaceous (Late Cret.)

Comanchean (Early Cret.)

Jurassic
  Late Juras.

  Medial Juras.

  Early Juras.

Triassic
  Late Trias.
  Medial Trias.
  Early Trias.
Permian
  Ochoa (Late Perm.)
  Guadalupian (Early and Late
  Perm.)
    Capitan
    Vidri
    Word

Kujalnic
Tretichnyi
  Pliotsen
    Cimmerian (also Warm Pontian)
    Pontian (restricted)
    Meotian (also early Pontian)
  Miocene
    Sarmatian
    Karaganian and Kanka
    Tarkhanian and Tekorakian
    Bardigacian and Helvetian
  Oligocene
  Eocene
  Paleocene
Late Cretaceous
  Danian
  Maestrichtian
  Campanian
  Santonian
  Turonian and Coniacian
  Cenomanian
Early Cretaceous
  Albian
  Hauterivian and Barremian
  Valanginian
Jurassic
  Late Jurassic
    Volgian (Tithonian)
    Kimeridgian
    Oxfordian
    Callovian
  Medial Jurassic
    Bathonian
    Bajocian
  Early Jurassic
    Aalenian
    Toarcian
Triassic
  Late Trias.
  Medial Trias.
  Early Trias.
Permian
  Tatarian

  Kazanian
  Ufimian
  Kungurian

Leonardian	Artinskian
	Sarana
	Sarga
	Irgina
	Burtsevka
	Sterlitamak
Wolfcampian (Lyonian)	Sakmarian
	Tastuba
	Kurmaia
	Assel
Late Pennsylvanian	Upper Carboniferous (Uralian)
Virgil	⎰ Orenburgian
	⎱ Gzhelian (Samarian)
Missouri	Kasimovan (Teguliferina zone)
Middle Pennsylvanian	Middle Carboniferous (Moskovian)
Des Moines	Myachkovo
	Podol
Atoka	Kashira
Early Pennsylvanian	
Morrow	Vereya
Springer	Bashkirian
Mississippian	Lower Carboniferous
Chester	Namurian
Meramek	
Osage	Visean
Kinderhook	Tournaisian
Devonian	Devonian
Upper Devonian	Upper Devonian
	Bureg
	Il'men'
Fammenian	Svinord
	Shelon'
	Chudovo
Frasnian	Pskov
	Snetogor
	Podsnetogor
	Oredezh
	Middle Devonian
Givetian	Luga (Luzhsky)
Eifelian	Narova

Provincial terms for the Paleogene (Early Tertiary) of Fergana (western part of Russian Turkestan). (After Gekker, Osipova, and Bel'skaya, 1963, Fig. 1 on p. 618.)

Fergana Stage	
Sumsar	Medial Oligocene
Khanabed	Early Oligocene
Sphara ⎱	
Rishtan ⎰	Upper Eocene
Turkestan	
Alai	Medial Eocene
Sogdiana Stage	
Suzak	Early Eocene
Bukhara	Paleocene

Prepared from various sources by M. K. Elias, Dec. 4, 1963

PLATE I

1. Burial in quiet conditions. Shell of *Lingula amalitzkii* Wen. with two valves connected and in life position, Svinord marl beds of Upper Devonian, in the Main Devonian Field, Shelon' River.
2. Burial in quiet conditions. Open shell of *Paracyclas rugosa* Goldf., with valves connected by ligament and not separated at time of burial. Fine-grained limestone, Buregi beds of Upper Devonian in the Main Devonian Field, Il'men' Lake.
3. Burial in disturbed conditions. Valves of *Lingula punctata* Hall, disconnected and with convex surface up. Marine near-shore red sandstone with crossbedding. Upper Devonian upper red beds in the Main Devonian Field, Syas' River.
4. Burial in disturbed conditions. Disconnected valves of *Chonetipustula ilmenica* Nal., with convex surface up (in ventral valve it is outer surface and in dorsal valve inner surface), detrital limestone, Pskov beds of Upper Devonian in the Main Devonian Field, Syas' River.

Photographs in natural size, unless otherwise indicated. Photographs of Plates I - XIII and XVII by P. S. Petrov, S. N. Zenkov, A. V. Skinder and other photographers. Plates XIV - XVI by the author and I. R. Gekker.

PLATE I 99

1

2

3

4

PLATE II

1. Fragmentary crinoid stems oriented parallel to crest of ripple marks, Chudovo beds of Upper Devonian in the Main Devonian Field, Chudovo.
2. Two specimens of *Pteroniscus* equally recurved by water action, lacustrine laminated calcareous dolomites ("paper shales") of Late Jurassic age, Kara-Tau paleontological preserve, southern Kazakhstan. × 0.5.
3. Accumulation of uniformly oriented shells of *Tentaculites glaber* Trd. washed together in Svinord beds of Upper Devonian, in the Main Devonian Field, Koloshka River. × 3.

PLATE II   101

1

2

3

PLATE III

1. Shell of *Athyris pectinifera* Sow. with circular hole drilled by predatory gastropod (*Naticopsis*?). Kazanian Stage of Permian System. Sok River. × 1.5.
2. Borings of worm *Palaeosabella* in *Mucrospirifer muralis* (Vern.) valve, initiated at its anterior edge during life (case of commensalism), Pskov beds of Upper Devonian in the Main Devonian Field, Syas' River. × 1.5.
3. Borings of *Polydora* worm in oyster shell *Ostrea* (*Platygena*) *asiatica* Rom., Rishtan Stage of Paleogene, South Fergana, Isfara River. × 2.
4. Shell of oyster *Fatina* densely riddled by rock-borer *Lithophaga*, Turkestan Stage of Paleogene, South Fergana, Rishtan.
5. Pelecypod *Lithophaga* in bored hole in shell of *Ostrea* (*Platygena*) *asiatica* Rom., Rishtan Stage of Paleogene, South Fergana, Isfara River.
6. Shell of *Turkostrea turkestanensis* (Rom.) with canals made by boring sponge *Cliona* (*Vioa*), Alai Stage of Paleogene, southwestern Fergana, Maydan Tau Range.

PLATE III   103

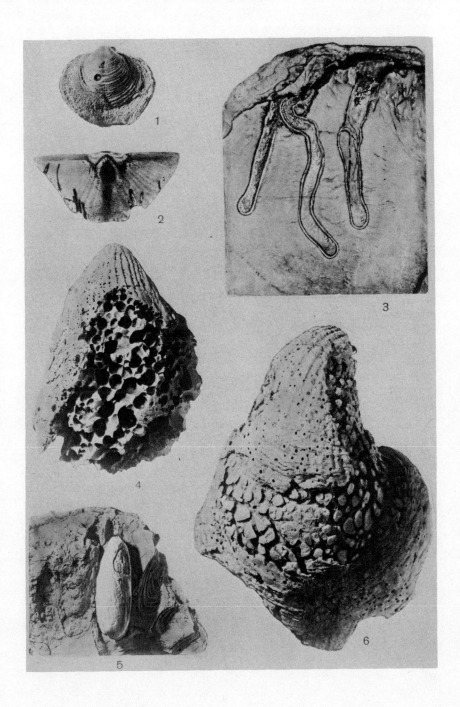

PLATE IV

1. Crinoid *Cromyocrinus simplex* Trd. with gastropod *Platyceras* attached above anal orifice of crinoid calyx, and feeding on crinoid excreta (illustrating coprophagy, a variety of commensalism), Middle Carboniferous, Moscow region (Ivanova, 1958).
2. Pathologic swelling of crinoid stem caused by parasite, which entered through a hole, Upper Carboniferous, Gzhel' town, × 2 (Ivanova, 1958).

3 and 4. Pathologic swelling of crinoid stems caused by parasites (3–showing hole through which parasite entered), Ordovician, Leningrad region (3 Volkhov River; 4, Syas' River). × 2.

5. Shell of *Parkinsonia parkinsoni* (Sow.) with healed injuries, Bajocian, Saratov region (Kamysheva-Elpat'-evskaya, 1951). × 0.7.
6. *Antiquatonia hindi* (Muir-Wood) with conspicuous injuries inflicted during its life, Lower Carboniferous, southern part of Moscow basin, Oka River (Sarycheva, 1949b).

7–11. Cases of commensalism and parasitism of bryozoan *Diplotrypa petropolitana* Pand. (*Mesotrypa excentrica* modzal), and worms (7–top view of bryozoan colony, with two small holes in its surface, representing outer ends of loop-curved tube of commensal worm located at its base. × 1.5; 8–another colony with lateral polished cut revealing one loop of tube. × 2; 9–polished cut of still another colony, showing two interruptions and resumptions of growth and containing two tubes, cut showing end of lower and upper tubes, and revealing their loops. × 2; 10, 11–bryozoan colony with protrusion terminated by single opening which leads into passage with blind end (case of parasitism), 11 revealing loop of worm-commensal tube. Kukruse beds, Ordovician, western part of Leningrad region. × 2).

PLATE IV   105

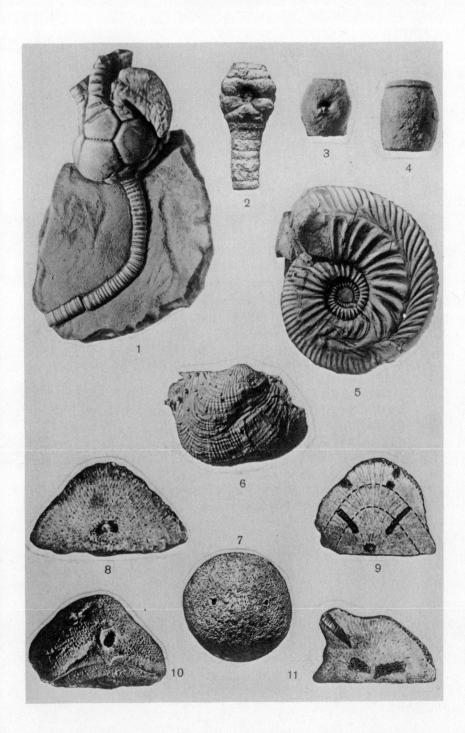

PLATE V

1. Life group of 13 individuals of *Camarotoechia strugi*
   Nal., Chudovo beds of Upper Devonian of the Main
   Devonian Field, Shelon' River.
2. Life group of *Theodossia tanaica* Nal. comprising 15
   individuals in various stages of growth, Upper Devonian
   in Central Devonian Field, Don River (Ivanova, 1949b).
3. *Cyrtospirifer tenticulum* (Vern.) attached to side of
   stromatoporoid (attachment subsequent to stromatoporoid death, under new life conditions), Bureg beds
   of Upper Devonian in the Main Devonian Field, Kukhva
   River (tributary of Velikaya River).
4. Settling of *Spirorbis omphalodes* Goldf. on valve of
   Cyrtospirifer schelonicus Nal., Svinord beds of Upper
   Devonian in the Main Devonian Field, Koloshka River.
   × 1.5.
5. Settling of *Serpula devonica* Pacht in oriented manner
   on valve of *Mucrospirifer muralis* (Vern.), Chudovo
   beds of Upper Devonian in the Main Devonian Field,
   Shelon' River. × 1.5.

PLATE V   107

PLATE VI

1. Holdfasts of crinoids, tubes of *Spirorbis omphalodes* Goldf. and outlets of *Trypanites* passages on abraded surface of limestone bed, Chudovo beds of Upper Devonian in the Main Devonian Field, Shelon' River. × 0.7.
2. Edrioasteroid *Lepidodiscus* sp. on abraded surface of limestone bed, Chudovo beds of Upper Devonian in the Main Devonian Field, Shelon' River. × 3.
3. Two specimens of pelecypod *Limanomia* adhering to abraded surface of limestone bed, Chudovo beds of Upper Devonian in the Main Devonian Field, Shelon' River.

PLATE VI 109

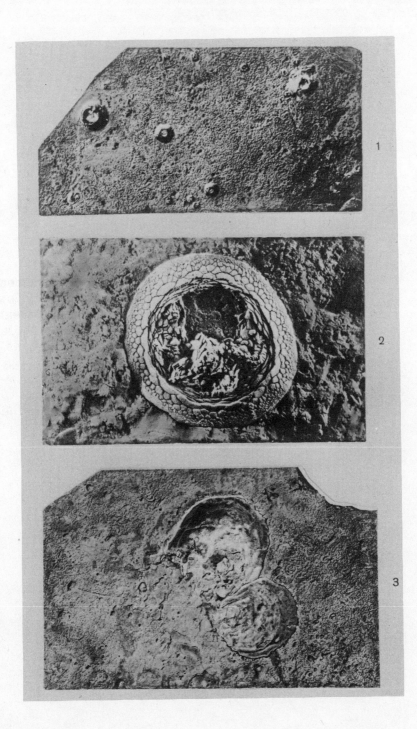

PLATE VII

1. Calcareous pebble covered on all sides by attached *Irboskites fixatus* Bekk., tubes of *Spirorbis omphalodes* Goldf., and holes of *Trypanites* (resting single dorsal valve of *Mucrospirifer muralis* (Vern.)). Pskov beds of Upper Devonian in the Main Devonian Field, Syas' River.
2. *Aulopora gekkeri* Tchern. colony and *Irboskites suchlovae* Nal. on abraded and *Trypanites*-bored surface of limestone bed, Chudovo beds of Upper Devonian in the Main Devonian Field, Shelon' River. × 4.

PLATE VII   111

1

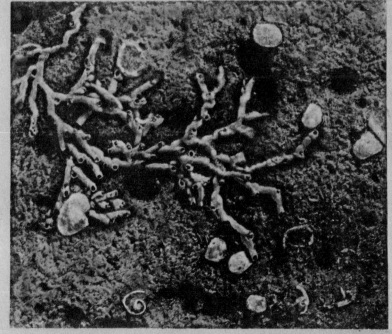

2

PLATE VIII

1. Calcareous pebble densely riddled by worm *Trypanites*, Pskov beds of Upper Devonian in the Main Devonian Field, Syas' River. × 1.5.
2. Densely spaced borings of *Trypanites* in hard limestone bottom, Pskov beds of Upper Devonian in the Main Devonian Field, Velikaya River, Vybuty Rapids. × 2. (Polished cut across bedding surface.)

PLATE VIII 113

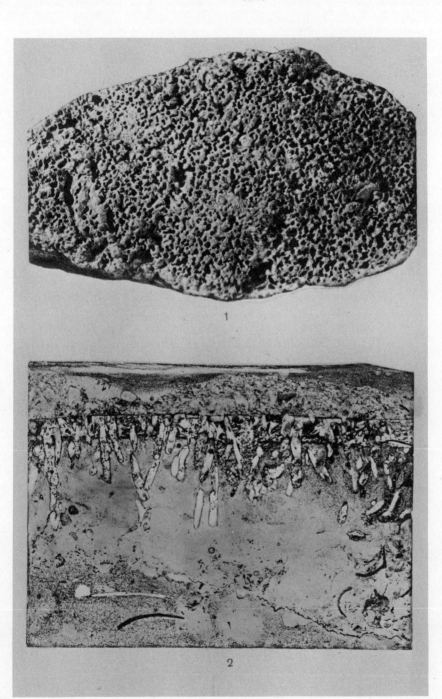

1

2

PLATE IX

1. Bars on lower surface of micaceous-calcareous siltstone bed, representing fillings of some borings made
on upper surface of underlying clay bed, Il'men' beds
of Upper Devonian in the Main Devonian Field, Il'men'
Lake. × 1.5.
2. Grooves formed by crawling invertebrates (worms?),
upper surface of siltstone, Pskov beds of Upper Devonian in the Main Devonian Field, Syas' River. × 1.5.

PLATE IX   115

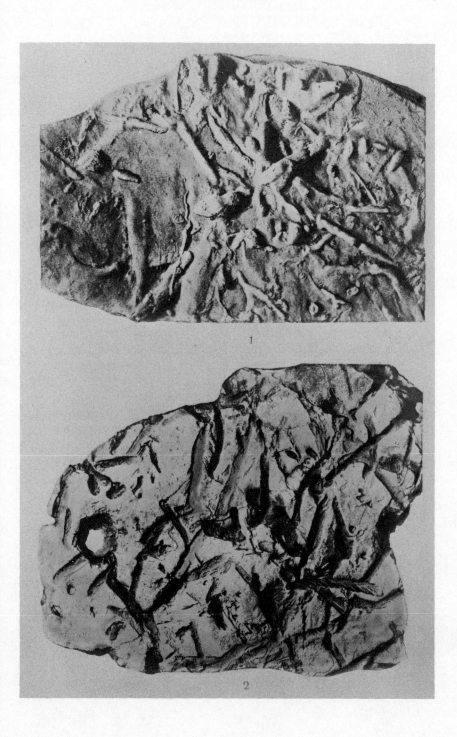

1

2

PLATE X

1. *Rhizocorallium devonicum* Gekker. Looplike tubes of
   burrowing invertebrates, apparently worms, parallel
   to bedding surface, in an intercalated-silty limestone,
   Pskov beds of Upper Devonian in the Main Devonian
   Field, Syas' River. × 0.3.
2. Fucoids. Branching tubes of earth-eaters, apparently
   worms, in a micaceous siltstone, intercalated in clays,
   Pskov beds of Upper Devonian in the Main Devonian
   Field, Syas' River.
3. Zoophycos (*Taonurus, Spirophyton*). Complex, looplike,
   spirally arranged passages of mud-eaters, apparently
   worms, in clayey detrital limestone, Lower Carboniferous of northwestern part of Moscow basin, Msta River,
   above Borovichi town. × 0.25.

PLATE X   117

1

2

3

PLATE XI

1 and 2. *Corophioides*. Fillings of looplike dugouts of
          burrowing invertebrates, apparently decapod
          crustaceans; wrinkles are traces of leg scratch-
          ing on sides of tube, Paleogene, Kazakh S.S.R.,
          Karakumy.
3. Rhizolith. Filling of straight tube of burrowing decapod
    crustacean with the same kind of wrinkles, Cretaceous-
    Paleogene border, Saratov region, Vol'sk town.
4. Helminthoids. Filling of winding passages of crawling
    animal, apparently worm, adjacent to each other on sea
    bottom, Flysch deposits, China, Sin'tszyan, Bagran-
    Kul' Lake. × 1.5.
5. *Caulerpites pennatus* Eichw. Bar with oblique wrinkles
    on lower surface of limestone bed. Chudovo beds of
    Upper Devonian in the Main Devonian Field, Syas'
    River. × 0.5.

PLATE XI   119

PLATE XII

1. *Coccolepis aniscowitchi* Gor. -Kulcz., with roe, Upper Jurassic lacustrine laminated calcareous dolomites ("paper shales"), Kara-Tau paleontological preserve, southern Kazakhstan.
2. Growth series of *Enteletes lamarckii* Fisch. (from very young through adult and gerontic shells), Kasimov horizon of Upper Carboniferous, "Krasnyy Stroitel'" plant on Moskva River (Ivanova, 1949a).
3. Shells of juvenile ammonites, probably *Aconeceras trautscholdi* (Sinz.), just hatched out of eggs, Lower Cretaceous, Volga River, Ul'yanovsk city. × 13.

PLATE XII   121

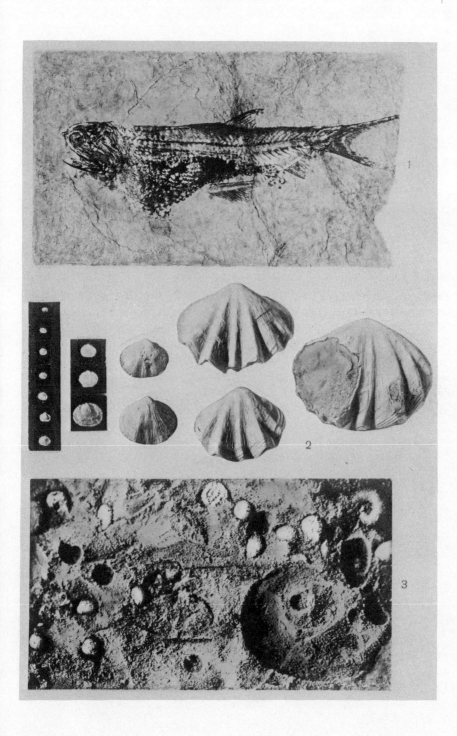

PLATE XIII

1. Shell of cephalopod *Parabelopeltis* ? sp. (suborder Teuthoidea) with preserved ink sac, filled with pigment (sepia). Lower Volga stage of Upper Jurassic, Kostroma region, Unzha River.
2. Carapace of *Phacops* (*Trimerocephalus*) *macrophthalmus* (Reinh. Richter), shed at molting, Famennian stage, Aktyubinsk region, Dzhangyz-Agach River. × 1.5. (Maksimova, 1955.)
3. Spider in amber, Lower Tertiary deposits, Kaliningrad region. × 8.
4. Bird feather on slab of lacustrine marl, Upper Tertiary, northern Kazakhstan, south of Kochkorka. × 1.5.

PLATE XIII   123

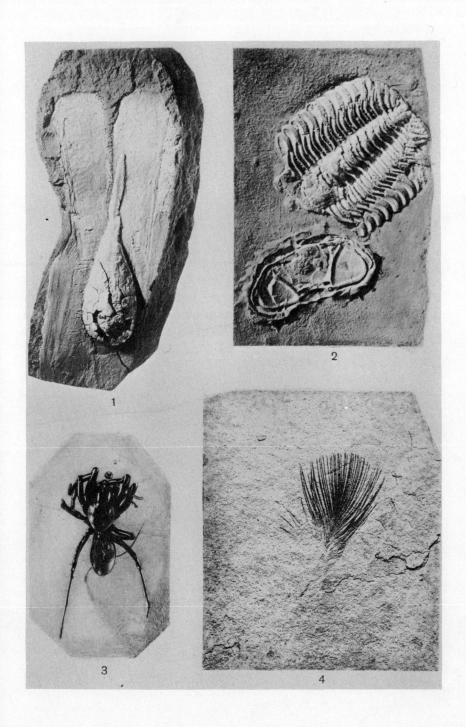

1

2

3

4

PLATE XIV

1. Tracks of Upper Cretaceous dinosaurs on surface of limestone bed, Sataplia hill near Kutaisi town (Sataplia preserve).
2. Ganoid fish *Pteroniscus* sp. in laminated calcareous dolomites ("paper shales"), deposits of Upper Jurassic lake, Kara-Tau paleontological preserve, southern Kazakhstan.

PLATE XIV   125

PLATE XV

1. Exposure showing mass of so-called rhizoliths: fillings
   of tubes made by burrowing decapod crustaceans *Callianassa*, in lower surface of siltstone bed cemented
   by carbonate, Suzak stage of Paleogene, southern Fergana, Isfara River.
2. Surface of rocky sea shore in Alai stage of Paleogene,
   smoothed over by tides and riddled by rock-borer
   Lithophaga, Tadzhik S.S.R., vicinity of Ura-Tyube town.

PLATE XV   127

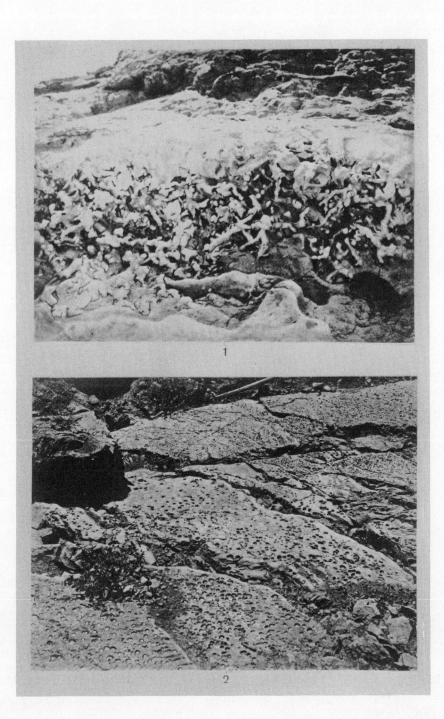

1

2

PLATE XVI

1 and 2. Field photographs showing two different planes,
         Paleogene, Turkestan Stage, northern Fergana.
         1—General view of oyster banks, interbedded
         with clays, and capped by limestones. 2—Details
         of one of the oyster beds.

PLATE XVI   129

1

2

130 PLATE XVII

PLATE XVII

Ancient life on part of hard smooth calcareous sea
bottom, Chudovo epoch. (Late Devonian sea in Main Devonian Field of Russian Platform.) Reconstruction on evidence of fauna found on the abraded surface of limestone
bed, adnate and encrusting (see Plate VI and Plate VII,
2). Paleontological Museum, Academy of Sciences of the
U.S.S.R. Part of exhibit on theme "Life in Devonian Sea."

PLATE XVII   131

Bibliography

Listed below are abbreviated names of institutions in serial publications
with their full explanation:

AN — Akademiya Nauk (in publications of the "AN SSSR")
MGRI — Moskovskiy Geologo-Razvedochnyy institut
MOIP — Moskovskoye obshchestvo ispytateley prirody
VNIGRI — Vsesoyuzn. Neftyanoy nauchno-issledov. geologo-razved. institut
VNIRO — Vsesoyuznyy nauchno-issledovatel'skiy institut rybnogo khozyaystva
i okeanografii
VSEGEI — Vsesoyuznyy nauchno-issledovatel'skiy Geologicheskiy institut

ABEL, O., 1912. Grundzüge der Paläobiologie der Wirbeltiere. Enke, Stuttgart.

ABEL, O., 1916. Paläobiologie der Cephalopoden aus der Gruppe der Dibranchiaten. Fischer, Jena.

ABEL, O., 1921. Die Methoden der paläobiologischen Forschung. Abderhaldens Handbuch der biologischen Arbeitsmethoden, 10 (2).

ABEL, O., 1927. Lebensbilder aus der Tierwelt der Vorzeit, 2-te Aufl. Fischer, Jena.

ABEL, O., 1929. Paläobiologie und Stammesgeschichte. Fischer, Jena.

ABEL, O., 1935. Vorzeitliche Lebensspuren. Fischer, Jena.

AGER, D.V., 1963. Principles of Paleoecology. McGraw-Hill, New York.

ALLEE, W.C., EMERSON, A.E., PARK, O., PARK, T. and SCHMIDT, K.P., 1950. Principles of animal ecology. Saunders, Philadelphia.

ANDRUSOV, N. I., 1896-1902. Die südrussischen Neogenablagerungen. 1-3 (34, 36, 39).

ANDRUSOV, N.I., 1897. Fossil and living *Dreissensidae* of Eurasia. Tr. St. Petersburg Society of Naturalists, Div. Geol. Mineral., Vol. 25. Iskopaemye i zhivushchie *Dreissensidae* Evrazii. Tr. SPb. obshch-va estestvoisp., otd. geol. i miner., t. 25.

ANDRUSOV, N.I., 1909-1912. Die fossilen *Bryozoenriffe* der Halbinseln Kertsch und Taman. 1-3. Kiev.

ANDRUSOV, N.I., 1961. Selected works, Vol. 1. Acad. Sci. U.S.S.R. Izbrannye trudy, t. 1. Izd. AN SSSR.

ARENDT, Yu. A., 1961. On damages to crinoids induced by *Schizoproboscina*. Paleontol. J., no. 2. O povrezhdeni-yakh morskich liliy, vyzvannykh *Schizoproboscina*.Paleontolog. Zhurnal, No. 2.

ARKHANGEL'SKIY, A.D., 1912. Upper Cretaceous deposits of eastern European Russia. Materials on the geology of Russia, Vol. 25.Verkhremelovye otlozheniya vostoka Evropeyskoy Rossii. Materialy dlya geologii Rossii, t. 25.

ARKHANGEL'SKIY, A.D., 1952. Selected works of Academician A.D. Arkhangel'skiy, Vol. 1. Acad. Sci. U.S.S.R. Izbrannye trudy akad. A.D. Arkhangel'skogo, t.1. Izd. AN SSSR.

ARKHANGEL'SKIY, A.D. and STRAKHOV, N.M., 1938. Geological structure and developmental history of the Black Sea. Acad. Sci. U.S.S.R. Geologicheskoe stroenie i istoriya razvitiya Chernogo morya. Izd. AN SSSR.

AUGUSTA, J. and REMEŠ, M., 1956. Uvód do všeobecné paleontologie. Praha.

BACHOFEN-ECHT, A., 1949. Der Bernstein und seine Einschlüsse. Wien.

BALDI, T., 1958. Paläoökologische Fazies-Analyse der burdigal-helvetischen Schichtreihe von Budafak in der Umgebung von Budapest. Ann. Univ. Sci. Budapest. Rolando Eotvos Nominatae, Sect. Geol., Vol. 2.

BEL'SKAYA, T.N., 1960. Late Devonian sea of Kuznetsk basin, its historical development, population, and deposits. Tr. Paleontol. Inst., Acad. Sci. U.S.S.R., Vol. 82. Pozdnedevonskoe more Kuznetskoy kotloviny, istoriya ego razvitiya, naselenie i osadki. Tr. Paleont. in-ta AN SSSR, t. 82.

BEL'SKAYA, T. N. and IVANIYA, V. A., 1955. Late Devonian coral-stromatoporid bioherm at Tom' River. Tr. Acad. Sci. U.S.S.R., 100(3). Korallovo-stroma-topovyy biogerm verkhnedevonskogo vozrasta na r. Tomi. Dokl. AN SSSR, t. 100, No. 3.

BERINGER, C. Ch., 1939. Paläobiologie. Bewegung, Umwelt und Gestalt fossiler Tiere. Stuttgart.

BIERNAT, G., 1961. *Diorygma atrypophilia* n. gen., n. sp.— a parasitic organism of *Atrypa zonata* Schnur. Acta Palaeontol. Polon., 4 (1).

BOBRINSKIY, N.A., ZENKEVICH, L.A. and BIRSHTEYN, Ya. A., 1946. Animal geography. Soviet Sci. Geografiya zhivotnykh. Sov. nauka.

BOLKHOVITINOVA, M.A., 1938. Ecology, paleogeography, and stratigraphic significance of the gigantells of Tula deposits of Moscow basin. Tr. MGRI, Vol. 12. Ekologiya, paleogeografiya i stratigraficheskaya tsennost' gigantell tul'skoy tolshchi Podmoskovnogo basseyna. Tr. MGRI, t. 12.

BORISYAK, A.A., 1916. On Walcott's discoveries in the Canadian Cambrian. Priroda, no. 3. O nakhodkakh Ch. Uol'kotta v kembriyskikh otlozheniyakh Kanady. "Priroda", No. 3.

BORISYAK, A.A., 1944. \Chalicotherium as a biological type. Zool. J., 23 (4). Khalikoteriy kak biologicheskiy tip. "Zoologicheskiy zhurnal", t. 23, vyp. 4.

BORISYAK, A.A., 1945a. Paleozoology: Twenty-five years of progress in biological science in the U.S.S.R., 1917-1942. Acad. Sci. U.S.S.R. Paleozoologiya. Uspekhi biologicheskikh nauk v SSSR za 25 let. 1917-1942. Izd. AN SSSR.

BORISYAK, A.A., 1945b. Basic problems of evolutionary paleontology. Bull. MOIP, New Ser., Vol. 50, Div. Geol., 20 (1-2). Osnovnye zadachi evolyutsionnoy paleontologii. Byull. MOIP, nov. ser., t. 50, otd. geol., t. 20, vyp. 1-2.

BORISYAK, A.A., 1947. Basic problems of evolutionary paleontology. Acad Sci. U.S.S.R. Osnovnye problemy evolyutsionnoy paleontologii. Izd. AN SSSR.

BUCHER, W., 1938. Key to papers published by an Institute for the study of modern sediments in shallow seas. J. Geol., Vol. 46.

BUSHINSKIY, G.I., 1954. Lithology of Cretaceous deposits of Dnepro-Donetsk depression. Tr. Inst. Geol. Sci., Acad. Sci. U.S.S.R., no. 156. Litologiya melovykh otlozheniy Dneprovsko-Donetskoy vpadiny. Tr. In-ta geol. nauk AN SSSR, vyp. 156.

BYKOVA, E.V., 1956. Devonian foraminifers and radiolarias of Volga-Uralian region. Tr. VNIGRI, New Ser., no. 87. Foraminifery i radiolyarii devona Volgo-Ural'skoy oblasti. Tr. VNIGRI, nov. ser., vyp. 87.

BYKOVA, N.K., 1959. Materials on foraminiferal paleoecology of Altai and Turkestan stages of Paleogene in

Fergana valley. Microfauna U.S.S.R., Collected works 10, Tr. VNIGRI. Materialy po paleoekologii foramini- fer altayskogo i turkestanskogo yarusov paleogena ferganskoy doliny. Mikrofauna SSSR, sb. 10, Tr. VNIGRI.

BYSTROV, A.P. and EFREMOV, I.A., 1940. *Benthosuchus sushkini* Efr.—Eotriassic labyrinthodont from Shar- zhenga River. Tr. Paleontol. Inst., Acad. Sci. U.S.S.R., 10 (1). *Benthosuchus sushkini* Efr.—labirintodont iz eotriasa reki Sharzhengi. Tr. Paleont. in-ta AN SSSR, t. 10, vyp. 1.

CHEDIYA, D.M., 1959. On some factors in abiotic medium which affect development of skeleton in Paleogene radiolaria of Tadzhik depression. Tr. Tadzhik State Univ., Ser. Nat. Sci., Vol. 2. O vliyanii nekotorykh faktorov abioticheskoy sredy na formirovanie skeletov paleogenovykh radiolyariy Tadzhikskoy depressii. Tr. Tadzhiksk. gos. un-ta, ser. estestv. nauk, t. 2.

CHERKESOV, V. Yu., 1936. Lower Silurian corals of Lenin- grad region. (Distribution and manner of life). Rept. Leningrad Mining Inst., 9 (2). Nizhnesiluriyskie korally Leningradskoy oblasti. (Rasprostranenie i obraz zhi- zni). Zap. Leningr. gorn. in-ta, t. 9, vyp. 2.

CLARKE, J. M., 1921. Organic Dependence and Disease: Their Origin and Significance. New Haven.

CLOUD, P.E., 1959. Paleoecology— retrospect and pros- pect. J. Paleontol., 33 (5).

DACQUÉ, E., 1921. Vergleichende biologische Formen- kunde der fossilen niederen Tiere. Berlin.

DAVITASHVILI, L. Sh., 1936. Toward the study of regular changes in body size in phylogenetic branches. Probl. Paleontol., Vol. 1. K izucheniyu zakonomernostey izmeneniy velichiny tela v filogeneticheskikh vetvyakh. Problemy paleontologii, t. 1.

DAVITASHVILI, L. Sh., 1937. Toward the history and ecol- ogy of molluscan faunas in Lower Pliocene marine basins. (Meotic-Lower Pontian). Probl. Paleontol., Vols. 2-3. K istorii i ekologii mollyuskovoy fauny morskikh basseynov nizhnego pliotsena (meotis-nizh- niy pont). Problemy paleontologii, t. 2-3.

DAVITASHVILI, L. Sh., 1943. Darwinism and problems of accumulation of combustible minerals. Bull. Natl. Mus., Georgia, Vol. 12-A. Darvinizm i problema nakopleniya goryuchikh iskopaemykh. "Vestn. gos. muzeya Gruzii", t. 12-A.

DAVITASHVILI, L. Sh., 1945. Cenoses of living organisms and of organic remains. (Suggestion for classification). Rept., Acad. Sci. Georgian S.S.R., 7 (7). Tsenozy zhivykh organizmov i organicheskikh ostatkov. (Opyt klassifikatsii). Soobshch. Akad. nauk Gruz. SSR, t.7, No. 7.

DAVITASHVILI, L. Sh., 1947. Ecogeny of types, classes and other subdivisions of the organic world. Ecogeny of life regions and of habitat types. Ecogenic processes of localized significance. Rept., Acad. Sci. Georgian S.S.R., 8 (5-7). Ekogeniya tipov, klassov i drugikh podrazdeleniy organicheskogo mira. Ekogeniya zhiznennykh oblastey i tipov mestoobitaniy. Ekogeneticheskie protsessy chastnogo znacheniya. Soobshch. Akad. nauk Gruz. SSR, t. 8, No. 5, No. 6, No. 7.

DAVITASHVILI, L. Sh., 1948. History of evolutionary paleontology from Darwin to our days. Inst. Hist. Nat. Sci., Acad. Sci. U.S.S.R. Istoriya evolyutsionnoy paleontologii ot Darvina do nashikh dney. Izd. In-ta istorii estestvoznaniya AN SSSR.

DEECKE, W., 1913-1915. Paläobiologische Betrachtungen. Neues Jahrb. Geol. Paläontol., 1913, 1914, 1915. Zentr. Mineral. Geol. Paläontol., 1913.

DEECKE, W., 1923. Die Fossilisation. Berlin.

DERYUGIN, K. M., 1913. Fauna of Kola Gulf and its life conditions. Rept. Acad. Sci. St. Petersburg, [8] 34 (1). Fauna Kol'skogo zaliva i usloviya ee sushchestvovaniya. Zap. AN SPb., 8 ser., 6. 34, No. 1.

DERYUGIN, K.M., 1928. Fauna of White Sea and its life conditions. Investigations of seas of U.S.S.R., nos. 7-8. Nat. Hydrol. Inst. Fauna Belogo morya i usloviya ee sushchestvovaniya. Issledovaniya morey SSSR. No. 7-8. Izd. Gos. Gidrolog. in-ta.

DINER, K., 1934. Fundamentals of biostratigraphy. State Mining, Geol., Petrol. Publ. Osnovy biostratigrafii. Gos. gorno-geol.-neftyan. izd-vo.

DOBROLYUBOVA, T. A., 1948. Variability of corals in phylogenetic group of *Dibunophyllum bipartitum* (McCoy)—*Caninia okensis* Stuck. Bull. Acad. Sci. U.S.S.R., Biol. Ser., no. 2. Izmenchivost' korallov filogeneticheskogo ryada *Dibunophyllum bipartitum* (McCoy)—*Caninia okensis* Stuck. Izv. AN SSSR., ser. biol., No. 2.

DOBROLYUBOVA, T.A., 1952. Morphogenesis in Lower Carboniferous corals *Lithostrotion* and *Lonsdaleia* in the light of Michurin's teaching. Bull. Acad. Sci. U.S.S.R., Biol. Ser., no. 6. Formoobrazovanie u nizhnekamennougol'nykh korallov *Lithostrotion* i *Lonsdaleia* v svete michurinskogo ucheniya. Izv. Akad. Nauk SSSR, biol. ser., No. 6.

DOLLO, L., 1909. La Paléontologie éthologique. Bull. Soc. Belge Géol., Paléontol. Hydrol., Vol. 23.

DUDICH, E., Jr., 1958. Paläogeographische und paläoökologische Verhältnisse der Budapester Umgebung im Obereozän und Unteroligozän. Ann. Univ. Sci. Budapest. Rolando Eotvos Nominatae, Sect. Geol., Vol. 2.

EBERZIN, A.G., 1949. Origin of the Pliocene cardiid genera in Evksinska basin. Tr. Paleontol. Inst., Acad. Sci. U.S.S.R., Vol. 20. O proiskhozhdenii pliotsenovykh rodov kardiid v Evksinskom basseyne. Tr. Paleont. in-ta AN SSSR, t. 20.

EFREMOV, I.A., 1950. Taphonomy and geological record. Vol. 1. Tr. Paleontol. Inst., Acad. Sci. U.S.S.R., Vol. 24. Tafonomiya i geologicheskaya letopis'. Kn. 1, Tr. Paleont. in-ta. AN SSSR, t. 24.

EHRENBERG, K., 1952. Paläobiologie und Stammesgeschichte. Ein Leitfaden. Wien.

ELIAS, M. K., 1937. Depth of deposition of the Big Blue (late Paleozoic) sediments in Kansas. Bull. Geol. Soc. Am., Vol. 48.

Field manual for petroleum geologists, 1954, Vol. 1. 2nd ed. Gostoptekhizdat. Sputnik polevogo geologa-neftyanika, 1954, t. 1. 2-e izd., Gostoptekhizdat.

FORSH, N. N., 1951. Paleontological regularities in distribution of Kazanian fauna in Middle Volga River. Geol. Collection, I (IV). Paleoekologicheskie zakonomernosti raspredeleniya fauny kazanskogo vremeni v Sredenem Povolzh'e. Geolog. sb., I (IV).

FORSH, N.N., 1955. Permian deposits. Ufimian suite and Kazanian stage. Series: Volga-Uralian petroliferous region. Tr. VNIGRI, New Ser., no. 92. Permskie otlozheniya. Ufimskaya svita i kazanskiy yarus. Seriya: Volgo-Ural'skaya neftenosnaya oblast'. Tr. VNIGRI, nov. ser., vyp. 92.

GABUNIYA, L.K., 1953. Study of mollusks in Middle Pliocene deposits of western Georgia. Tr. Paleobiol.
Dept., Georgian S.S.R., Vol. 1. K izucheniyu mollyuskov srednepliotsenovykh otlozheniy Zapadnyy Gruzii.
Tr. Sektora paleobiologii AN Gruzinskoy SSR, t. 1.

GABUNIYA, L. K., 1958. Dinosaur remains. Acad. Sci.
U.S.S.R. Sledy dinozavrov. Izd. AN SSSR.

GEKKER, E. L. and GEKKER, R. F., 1955. *Teuthoidea*
remains from Upper Jurassic and Lower Cretaceous
of Volga River. Probl. Paleontol., Vol. 2. Ostatki *Teuthoidea* iz verkhney yury i nizhnego mela Povolzh'ya.
Voprosy paleontologii, t. 2.

GEKKER, R. F., 1928. Paleobiological observations on
Lower Silurian invertebrates, I. Ann. Russ. Paleontol.
Soc., Vol. 7 (1927). Paleobiologicheskie nablyudeniya
nad nizhnesiluriyskimi bespozvonochnymi, I. Ezhegodnik Russkogo paleont. obshch-va, t. 7 (1927).

GEKKER, R. F., 1933. Principles and instruction for paleoecological investigations. Northwestern Geol. Prospecting Trust. Polozheniya i instruktsiya dlya ussle-
dovaniy po paleoekologii. Izd. Sev.-zap. geol.-razved.
tresta.

GEKKER, R. F., 1935a. Phenomena of overgrowth and at-
tachment in Upper Devonian fauna and flora of Main
Devonian Field. (Essays on ethology and ecology of
Paleozoic sea populations in Russian Platform, I).
Tr. Paleozool. Inst., Acad. Sci. U.S.S.R., Vol. 4.
Yavleniya prirastaniya i prikrepleniya sredi verkhne-
devonskoy fauny i flory Glavnogo devonskogo polya.
(Ocherki po etologii i ekologii naseleniya paleozoyskikh
morey Russkoy platformy, I). Tr. Paleozool. in-ta
AN SSSR, t. 4.

GEKKER, R. F., 1935b. Life in Devonian sea. Paleontol.
Mus., Acad. Sci. U.S.S.R. Zhizn' v devonskom more.
Izd. Paleont. muzeya AN SSSR.

GEKKER, R. F., 1938a. Organization of paleoecological
study of Lower Carboniferous of Leningrad region.
Materials on regional and applied geology of Leningrad region and Karelian A.S.S.R., Collected works,
no. 2. Leningr. Geological Trust. K postanovke paleoekologicheskogo izucheniya nizhnego karbona Leningradskoy oblasti. Mater. po region. i prikl. geologii
Len. obl. i Karel'skoy ASSR, sb. No. 2. Izd. Len. geol.
tresta.

GEKKER, R. F., 1938b. Cross section of interstratified part (a) okskoy suite, Lower Carboniferous on Msta River. Materials on regional and applied geology of Leningrad region and Karelian A.S.S.R., Collected works, no. 2. Leningrad Geol. Trust. Razrez tolshchi pereslaivaniya (a) okskoy svity nizhnego karbona na r. Mste. Mater. po region. i prikl. geologii Len. obl. i Karel'skoy ASSR, sb. No. 2. Izd. Len. geol. Tresta.

GEKKER, R. F. 1940a. Investigations of Carboniferous paleoecological expedition, 1934-1936. Tr. Paleontol. Inst., Acad. Sci. U.S.S.R., 9 (4). Raboty karbonovoy paleoekologicheskoy ekspeditsii 1934-1936 gg. Tr. Paleont. in-ta AN SSSR, t. 9, vyp. 4.

GEKKER, R. F.1940b. Paleontological and paleoecological expositions. Priroda, no. 1. Paleontologicheskie i paleoekologicheskie exspozitsii. "Priroda", No. 1.

GEKKER, R. F., 1941a. Deposits, fauna, and flora of Main Devonian Field. Fauna of Main Devonian Field, I. Paleontol. Inst., Acad. Sci. U.S.S.R. Otlozheniya, fauna i flora Glavnogo devonskogo polya. Fauna Glavnogo devonskogo polya, I. Izd. Paleont. in-ta AN SSSR.

GEKKER, R. F., 1941b. Paleoecological problems in working out of problems of organic evolution. Bull. Acad. Sci. U.S.S.R., Biol. Ser., no. 1. Zadachi paleoekologii v razrabotke problemy evolyutsii organicheskogo mira. Izd. AN SSSR, ser. biol., No. 1.

GEKKER, R. F., 1948a. Examples of paleoecological studies of sedimentary rocks. Collected lithologic works, I. VNIGRI. Primery paleoekologicheskogo izucheniya osadochnykh tolshch. Litolog. sb., I. Izd. VNIGRI.

GEKKER, R. F., 1948b. Current problems of paleoecology. Bull. MOIP, New Ser., Vol. 53, Div. Geol., 23 (1). Ocherednye problemy paleoekologii. Byull. MOIP, nov. ser., t. 53, otd. geol., t. 23, vyp. 1.

GEKKER, R. F., 1953a. Stratigraphy and fauna of Upper Devonian, Main Devonian Field of Russian Platform, and its facieological changes. Collection "Devonian of Russian Platform," VNIGRI. Stratigrafiya i fauna verkhnego devona Glavnogo devonskogo polya Russkoy platformy i ego fatsial'nye izmeneniya. Sb. "Devon Russkoy platformy," izd. VNIGRI.

GEKKER, R. F., 1953b. Oysters and oyster grounds in the Paleogene of Fergana (paleoecologic-evolution analysis). Bull. MOIP, New Ser., Vol. 58, Div. Geol., 28 (3). Ustritsy i ustrichniki ferganskogo paleogena (paleoekologo-evolyutsionyy analiz). Byull. MOIP, nov. ser., t. 58, otd. geol., t. 28, vyp. 3.

GEKKER, R. F., 1954a. Correlation of the sections of eastern and western halves of the Main Devonian Field, and basic ecological characters of its fauna and flora. Bull. Acad. Sci. U.S.S.R., Geol Ser., no. 4. Sopostavlenie razrezov vostochnoy i zapadnoy polovin Glavnogo devonskogo polya i osnovnye cherty ekologii ego fauny i flory. Izv. AN SSSR, ser. geol., No. 4.

GEKKER, R. F., 1954b, 1955. Instruction for paleoecological investigations. 1st and 2nd ed. Paleontol. Inst, Acad. Sci. U.S.S.R. Nastavlenie dlya issledovaniy po paleoekologii. 1-e i 2-e izd. Paleont. in-ta AN SSSR.

GEKKER, R. F., 1956. Aims and methods of paleoecological investigations in the U.S.S.R. Rept. 20th Intl. Geol. Congr., Mexico, 1956.

GEKKER, R. F., 1956a. Problems of biostratigraphic methods. Geological collection, nos. 2-3. L'vov Geol. Soc. K voprosu o metodakh biostratigrafii. Geol. sb. No. 2-3. L'vovskogo geol. obshch-va.

GEKKER, R. F., 1956b. Some problems of paleoecology and organization of paleoecological explorations. (Answer to critics). Geol. collection, nos. 2-3. L'vov Geol. Soc. O nekotorikh voprosakh paleoekologii i organizatsii paleoekologicheskikh issledovaniy. (Otvet kritikam). Geol. sb. No. 2-3. L'vovskogo geol. obshch-va.

GEKKER, R. F., 1956c. Ecological analysis of crustacean decapodes in Fergana Bay of Central Asia. Bull. MOIP, New Ser., Vol. 61, Div. Geol., 31 (1). Ekologicheskiy analiz desyatinogikh rakoobraznykh Ferganskogo zaliva paleogenovogo morya Sredney Azii. Byull. MOIP, nov. ser., t. 61, otd. geol., t. 31, vyp. 1.

GEKKER, R. F., 1960. Fossil fauna of smooth rocky marine bottom. (On types of rocky marine bottom). Tr. Geol. Inst., Acad. Sci. Estonian S.S.R., Vol. 5. Iskopaemaya fauna gladkogo kamennogo morskogo dna. (K voprosu o tipakh kamennogo morskogo dna). Tr. In-ta geologii AN Est. SSR, t. 5.

GEKKER, R. F., 1961. Complete utilization of paleontological possibilities in geology. Tr. 5th Session

All-Union Paleontol. Soc. Za polnoe ispol'zovanie voz-
mozhnostey paleontologii v geologii. Tr. 5-oy sessii
Vsesoyuzn. Paleontol. ob-va.

GEKKER, R. F. and MERKLIN, P. L., 1946. Peculiarities
of fish burial in Maikop clayey shales in Northern
Ossetia. Bull. Acad. Sci. U.S.S.R., Div. Biol. Sci.,
no. 6. Ob osobennostyakh zakhoroneniya ryb v maykop-
skikh glinistykh slantsakh Severnoy Osetii. Izv. AN
SSSR, otd. biol. nauk, No. 6.

GEKKER, R. F. and OSIPOVA, A. I., 1951. Problems of
state and development of Soviet lithology. Bull. Acad.
Sci. U.S.S.R., Geol. Ser., no. 3. K voprosu o sostoyanii
i razvitii sovetskoy litologii. Izv. AN SSSR, ser.
geol., No. 3.

GEKKER, R. F. and OSIPOVA, A. I., 1957. Observations
of organic remains. Collection "Methods in study of
sedimentary rocks," 1957, chapter 4. Gosgeoltekhizdat, Moscow. Nablyudeniya nad organicheskimi ostatkami. Sb. "Metody izucheniya osadochnykh porod."
Glava 4-ya. Gosgeoltekhizdat.

GEKKER, R. F., OSIPOVA, A. I. and BEL'SKAYA, T. N.,
1952. 1. The Fergana Bay of the Paleogene sea, its
development, precipitation, fauna and flora and their
conditions and habitations. 2. Ecologic characteristics
of population of the Fergana Bay of the Paleogene
sea. Bull. MOIP, New Ser., Vol. 57, Div. Geol., 27 (4).
1. Ferganskiy zaliv paleogenovogo morya, istoriya ego
razvitiya, osadki, fauna i flora i usloviya ikh obitaniya. 2. Ekologicheskaya kharakteristika naseleniya
Ferganskogo zaliva paleogenovogo morya. Byull.
MOIP, nov. ser., t. 57, otd. geol., t. 27, vyp. 4.

GEKKER, R. F., OSIPOVA, A. I. and BEL'SKAYA, T. N.,
1960. Fergana Bay of Paleogene sea, its history,
deposits, fauna and flora, and the conditions of their
habitat and development. Rept. Sov. Geologists, 21st
Intl. Geol. Congr., Copenhagen. Ferganskiy zaliv
paleogenovogo morya, ego istoriya, osadki, fauna,
flora, usloviya ikh i razvitiya. Mezhdunar. geol.
kongress, 21 sessiya. Doklady sovetsk. geologov.

GEKKER, R. F., OSIPOVA, A. I. and BEL'SKAYA, T. N.,
1961. Fergana Bay of Paleogene sea of Central Asia,
its history, deposits, fauna, flora, and conditions of
their habitat and development. Paleontol. Inst., Acad.

Sci. U.S.S.R., Vols. 1 and 2. Ferganskiy zaliv paleogenovogo morya Sredney Azii, ego istoriya, osadki,
fauna, flora, usloviya ikh obitaniya i razvitie. Izd.
Paleont. in-ta AN SSSR, kn. 1 i 2.

GEKKER, R. F., OSIPOVA, A. I. and BEL'SKAYA, T. N.,
1963. Fergana Gulf of Paleogene sea of Central Asia,
its history, sediments, fauna, and flora, their environment and evolution. Bull. Am. Assoc. Petrol. Geologists, 4 F (4).

GEKKER, R. F., RYABININ, A. N., RAMMEL'MEYER,
E. S. and FILLIPOVA, M. F., 1948. Ancient Jurassic
lake in Kara-Tau Range. Tr. Paleontol. Inst., Acad.
Sci. U.S.S.R., 15 (1). Iskopaemoe yurskoe ozero v
khrebte Kara-Tau. Tr. Paleont. in-ta AN SSSR, t. 15,
vyp. 1.

GEPTNER, V. G., 1936. General zoogeography. Biomedgiz.
Obshchaya zoogeografiya. Biomedgiz.

GERASIMOV, N. P., 1953. Some factors in origin of species
and their stratigraphic significance. Materials of paleontological conference on Paleozoic, May 14-17, 1951.
Paleontol. Inst., Acad. Sci. U.S.S.R. O nekotorykh
faktorakh vidoobrazovaniya i o znachenii ikh dlya
stratigrafii. Mater. paleont. soveshchaniya po paleozoyu 14-17 maya 1951 g. Izd. Paleont. in-ta AN SSSR.

Guide for travelers and ethnographers, 1950. Vol. 2. Geografizdat, Moscow. Spravochnik puteshestvennika i
kraeveda. 1950, t. 2. Geografizdat.

GUR'YANOVA, Ev., ZAKS, Iv. and USHAKOV, P., 1928-
1930. Littoral of Kola Gulf, I-III. Tr. Leningrad Soc.
Naturalists, 58 (2) 1928; 59 (2) 1929; 60 (2) 1930.
Littoral' Kol'skogo zaliva, I-III. Tr. Leningr. obshch-
va estestvoisp., t. 58, vyp. 2, 1928; t. 59, vyp. 2,
1929; t. 60, vyp. 2, 1930.

GUSTOMESOV, V. A., 1961. Ecology of Upper Jurassic
belemnites (climatic zonation in their distribution,
life habit, and common life injuries). Tr. Moscow Geol.
Prospecting Inst., Vol. 37, Geology and Prospecting.
K ekologii verkhneyurskikh belemnitov (klimatiches-
kaya zonal'nost' v rasprostranenii, obraz zhizni,
massovye prizhiznennye povrezhdeniya). Tr. Mosk.
Geol. razv. in-ta, t. 37, geol. i razvedka.

HÄNTSCHEL, W., 1955. Lebensspuren als Kennzeichen
des Sedimentationsraumes. Geol. Rundschau, 43 (2).

HÄNTSCHEL, W., 1955. Rezente und fossile Lebensspuren, ihre Deutung und geologische Auswertung. Experientia, 11 (10).

HÄNTSCHEL, W., 1956. Rückschau auf die paläontologischen und neontologischen Ergebnisse der Forschungsanstalt "Senckenberg am Meer." Senckenbergiana Lethaea, 37 (3-4).

HAUFF, B., 1921. Untersuchung der Fossilfundstätten von Holzmaden im Posidonienschiefer des oberen Lias Württembergs. Palaeontographica, Sect. B, Vol. 64.

HAUFF, B., 1953. Das Holzmadenbuch. Öhringen.

HEDGPETH, I. W., 1953. An introduction to the zoogeography of the northwestern Gulf of Mexico with reference to the invertebrate fauna. Publ. Inst. Marine Sci., 3 (1).

HESSE, R., ALLEE, W. C. and SCHMIDT, K. P., 1951. Ecological animal geography. 2nd ed.

IMBRIE, J. and NEWELL, N. (Ed.), 1964. Approaches to Paleoecology. Wiley, New York.

IVANOVA, E. A., 1941. Effects of natural selection on distribution and development of some brachiopods in Carboniferous of Moscow Basin. Bull. Acad. Sci. U.S.S.R., Biol. Ser., no. 1. O proyavlenii estestvennogo otbora na rasprostranenii i razvitii nekotorykh brakhiopod v karbone Podmoskovskoy kotloviny. Izv. AN SSSR, ser. biol., No. 1.

IVANOVA, E. A., 1947. Biostratigraphy of Middle and Upper Carboniferous in Moscow Basin. Tr. Paleontol. Inst., Acad. Sci. U.S.S.R., 12 (1). Biostratigrafiya srednego i verkhnego karbona Podmoskovnoy kotloviny. Tr. Paleont. in-ta AN SSSR, t. 12, vyp. 1.

IVANOVA, E. A., 1949a. Ontogeny of some Carboniferous brachiopods. Tr. Paleontol. Inst., Acad. Sci. U.S.S.R., Vol. 20. Ontogenez nekotorykh Kamennougol'nykh brakhiopod. Tr. Paleont. in-ta AN SSSR, t. 20.

IVANOVA, E. A., 1949b. Conditions of existence, mode of life, and historical development of some Middle and Upper Carboniferous brachiopods in Moscow Basin. Tr. Paleontol. Inst., Acad. Sci. U.S.S.R., Vol. 21. Usloviya sushchestvovaniya, obraz zhizni i istoriya razvitiya nekotorykh brakhiopod srednego i verkhnego karbona Podmoskovnoy kotloviny. Tr. Paleont. in-ta AN SSSR, t. 21.

IVANOVA, E. A., 1953. Detailed correlation of marine

deposits on their faunal evidence. Materials of paleontological conference on Paleozoic, May 14-17, 1951. Paleontol. Inst., Acad. Sci. U.S.S.R. Detal'noe sopostavlenie morskikh otlozheniy po faune. Mater. paleont. soveshchaniya po Paleozoyu 14-17 maya 1951 g. Izd. Paleont. in-ta AN SSSR.

IVANOVA, E. A., 1955. Correlation problem of connecting evolutionary stages of organic world with evolutionary stages of earth crust. Rept. Acad. Sci. U.S.S.R., 105 (1). K voprosu o svyazi etapov evolyutsii organicheskogo mira s etapami evolyutsii zemnoy kory. Dokl. AN SSSR, t. 105, No. 1.

IVANOVA, E. A., 1958a. Faunal development in connection with conditions of existence. Tr. Paleontol. Inst., Acad. Sci. U.S.S.R., Vol. 69. Razvitie fauny v svyazi s usloviyami sushchestvovaniya. Tr. Paleont. in-ta AN SSSR, t. 69.

IVANOVA, E. A., 1958b. Développement de la faune en relation avec les conditions d'existence. Livre de la série: Développement de la faune marine en Carbonifère moyen et supérieur dans la partie occidentale du syneclise en Moscou en relation avec l'histoire géologique. Tr. Inst. Paleontol., Acad. Sci. U.S.S.R., Vol. 69. Edit. Bureau de recherches géol. et minières, Service d'information géologique.

IVANOVA, E. A., 1959. Ways of development of paleoecology in the U.S.S.R. Paleontol. J., no. 2. O putyakh razvitiya paleoekologii v SSSR. Paleont. zhurn., No. 2.

IVANOVA, E. A., 1962. Ecology and development of brachiopods in Silurian and Devonian of Kuznetsk, Minusinsk, Tuvinsk basins. Tr. Paleontol. Inst., Acad. Sci. U.S.S.R. Ekologiya i razvitie brakhiopod silura i devona Kuznetskogo, Minusinskogo i Tuvinskogo basseynov. Tr. Paleont. in-ta AN SSSR.

IVANOVA, E. A. and KHVOROVA, I. V., 1955. Stratigraphy of Middle and Upper Carboniferous in western part of Moscow Basin. Tr. Paleontol. Inst., Acad. Sci. U.S.S.R., Vol. 53. Stratigrafiya srednego i verkhnego karbona zapadnoy chasti Moskovskoy sineklizy. Tr. Paleont. in-ta AN SSSR, t. 53.

KABANOV, K. A., 1959. How hard was rostrum of belemnite in live animals? Paleontol. J., no. 2. Byl li rostr belemnite tverdym pri zhizni zhivotnogo?

Paleont. zhurn., No. 2.

KAMYSHEVA-ELPAT'EVSKAYA, V. G., 1951. Shell damages during life of Jurassic ammonites. Sci. Rept.
Saratov State University, Geol. Div., Vol. 28. O
prizhiznennykh povrezhdeniyakh rakovinyurskikh am-
monitov. Uch. zap. Sarat. gos. un-ta, t. 28 (ser. geol.).

KAPTARENKO-CHERNOUSOVA, O. K., 1951. Kiev stage
and elements of its paleogeography. Tr. Inst. Geol.
Sci., Acad. Sci. Ukr. S.S.R., Ser. Stratigr. Paleontol.,
no. 3. Kievskiy yarus i elementy ego paleogeografii.
Tr. In-ta geol. nauk AN USSR, ser. stratigr. i paleont.,
vyp. 3.

KASHKAROV, D. N., 1945. Fundamentals of animal ecology.
2nd ed. Uchpedgiz. Osnovy ekologii zhivotnykh. 2-e izd.
Uchpedgiz.

KAZAKOVA, V. P., 1952. Stratigraphy and fauna of the
pelecypod mollusks of the Middle Miocene deposits of
Opol'ye (Western Ukraine). Tr. MGRI, Vol. 27.
Stratigrafiya i fauna plastinchatozhabernykh mollyuskov srednemiotsenovykh otlozheniy Opol'ya (Zapad-
naya Ukraina). Tr. MGRI, t. 27.

KHABAKOV, A. V., 1932. Finding of radiolarian fauna in
Paleozoic cherty slates and jaspers of Caucasian
Range and its paleogeographic significance. Rept.
All-Union Geol. Prospecting Assoc., 51 (13). O nakhodke
fauny radiolyariy v kremnistykh slantsakh i yashmakh
paleozoya Kavkazskogo khrebta i ee paleogeografi-
cheskom znachenii. Izv. Vses. geol.-razv. ob"edin.,
t. 51, vyp. 12.

KHABAKOV, A. V., 1937. Radiolarian fauna from Lower
Cretaceous and Upper Jurassic phosphorites in upper
Vyatka and Kama rivers basin. Ann. All-Russ. Paleontol. Soc., Vol. 11 (1934-1935). Fauna radiolyariy
iz nizhnemelovykh i verkhneyurskikh fosforitov basseyna verkhney Vyatki i Kamy. Ezhegodnik Vseross.
paleont. obshch-va, t. 11 (1934-1935).

KHVOROVA, I. V., 1953. Developmental history of Middle
and Upper Carboniferous sea in western part of Moscow Basin. Tr. Paleontol. Inst., Acad. Sci. U.S.S.R.,
Vol. 43. Istoriya razvitiya sredne- i verkhnekamennougol'nogo morya zapadnoy chasti Moskovskoy sineklizy. Tr. Paleont. in-ta AN SSSR, t. 43.

KHVOROVA, I. V., 1955. Some surficial textures in Upper

Carboniferous and Lower Permian flysch of southern
Ural. Tr. Inst. Geol. Sci., Acad. Sci. U.S.S.R., no. 155,
Geol. Ser., no. 66. O nekotorykh poverkhnostnykh
teksturakh v kamennougol'nom i nizhneperniskom
flishe Yuzhnogo Urala. Tr. In-ta geol. nauk AN SSSR,
vyp. 155, geol. ser. (No. 66).

KNIPOVICH, N. M., 1938. Hydrology of seas and brackish
waters (in connection with industrial utilization).
VNIRO. Gidrologiya morey i solonovatykh vod (v
primenenii k promyslovomu delu). Izd. VNIRO.

KOLESNIKOV, V. P., 1935. Sarmatian mollusks. Paleontol.
U.S.S.R., 10 (2). Sarmatskie mollyuski. Paleontologiya
SSSR, t. 10, ch. 2.

KOLESNIKOV, V. P., 1947. Problems of struggle and co-
existence in paleontology. Rept. Acad. Sci. U.S.S.R.,
58 (7). Problema bor'by i sozhitel'stva v paleontologii.
Dokl. AN SSSR, t. 58, No. 7.

KOLESNIKOV, V. P., 1948. On transition. Rept. Acad. Sci.
U.S.S.R., 61 (2). O tranzitsii. Dokl. AN SSSR, t. 61,
No. 2.

KOLESNIKOV, V. P., 1949. Some paleontological problems.
Bull. MOIP, New Ser., Vol. 54, Div. Geol., 24 (3).
O nekotorykh problemakh paleontologii. Byull. MOIP,
nov. ser. t. 54, otd. geol., 6. 24, vyp. 3.

KOLESNIKOV, V. P., ZHIZHCHENKO, B. P. and EBERZIN,
A. G., 1940. Neogene of U.S.S.R. Stratigraphy U.S.S.R.,
Vol. 12. Inst. Geol. Sci., Acad. Sci. U.S.S.R. Neogen
SSSR. Stratigrafiya SSSR, t. 12. Izd. IGN AN SSSR.

KÖNIGSWALD, R., 1930. Die Arten der Einregelung ins
Sediment bei den Seesternen und Seelilien des unter-
devonischen Bundenbacher Schiefers. Senckenbergiana, Vol. 12.

KOROBKOV, I. A., 1947. Analysis of molluscan fauna in
oil-producing Maikop suite. Bull. Leningrad Univ.,
no. 5. Analiz fauny mollyuskov neftenosnoy may-
kopskoy svity. "Vestn. Leningr. un-ta," No. 5.

KOROBKOV, I. A., 1949. Basic information on complex of
new species of Middle Eocene mollusks in northern
Caucasus, and conditions of their habitat. Bull. Leningrad Univ., no. 3. Osnovnye svedeniya o komplekse
novykh vidov sredneeotsenovykh mollyuskov Sever-
nogo Kavkaza i ob usloviyakh ikh obitaniya. Vestn.
Leningr. un-ta, No. 3.

KOROBKOV, I. A., 1950. Introduction to study of fossil mollusks. Inst. Earth Crust, Leningrad Univ. Vvedenie v izuchenie iskopaemykh mollyuskov. Izd. In-ta zemnoy kory. Leningr. gos. un-ta.

KOROLYUK, I. K., 1952. Podolian "toltry" and conditions of their development. Tr. Inst. Geol. Sci., Acad. Sci. U.S.S.R., no. 110,, Geol. Ser., no. 56. Podol'skie toltry i usloviya ikh obrazovaniya. Tr. In-ta geol. nauk AN SSSR, vyp. 110, ser. geol. (56).

KOVALEVSKIY, V. O., 1950. Collected scientific works, Vol. 1. Acad. Sci. U.S.S.R. Sobranie nauchnykh trudov, t. 1. Izd. AN SSSR.

KREJCI-GRAF, K., 1932. Definition der Begriffe Marken, Spuren, Fährten, Bauten, Hieroglyphen und Fucoiden. Senckenbergiana, 14 (1).

KUCHULORIYA, Kh. D., 1959. Habitat conditions of fauna in Akhaltsykh Upper Eocene basin. Bull. Leningrad Univ., no. 24, Ser. Geol. Geograph., no. 4. Ob usloviyakh obitaniya fauny v Akhaltsikhskom verkhne-eotsenovom basseyne. Vestn. Leningr. gos. un-ta, No. 24, ser. geol. i geografii, vyp. 4.

KUDRIN, L. N., 1957. Paleontological investigation of lower horizon deposits, Lower Tortonian in southwestern proximity of Russian Platform. Collected geological works, no. 4. L'vov Geol. Soc. O paleontologicheskikh issledovaniyakh otlozheniy nizhnego gorizonta nizhnego tortona yugo-zapadnoy okrainy Russkoy platformy. Geol. sb. No. 4. L'vovskogo geol. obshch-va.

LADD, H. S., 1959. Ecology, Palaeontology and Stratigraphy. Science, 129 (3341).

LECOMPTE, M., 1956. Quelques précisions sur le phénomène récifal dans le Dévonien de l'Ardenne et sur le rythme sédimentaire dans lequel il s'intègre. Inst. roy. Sci. nat. Belg. Bull., 32(21).

LECOMPTE, M., 196 . Compte rendu de la session extraordinaire de la Société Géologique de Belgique et de la Société belge de Géologie, de Paléontologie et d'Hydrologie du 25 au 28 septembre 1959.

LESSERTISSEUR, J., 1955. Traces fossiles d'activité animale et leur signification paléobiologique. Mém. Soc. Géol. France, [N.S.] 34 (4).

LIBROVICH, L. S., 1929. *Uralonema karpinskii* n. gen., n. sp. and other siliceous sponges from Carboniferous deposits of eastern slope of Urals. Tr. Geol. Comm., New Ser., no. 179. *Uralonema karpinskii* nov. gen. nov. sp. i drugie kremnevye gubki iz kamennougol'-nykh otlozheniy vostochnogo sklona Urala. Tr. Geol. Kom., nov. ser., vyp. 179.

LIVEROVSKAYA, E. V., 1951. Paleoecological study of Chokrak deposits in Dagestan. Collected geological works, no. 1 (IV). VNIGRI. Paleoekologicheskoe izuchenie chokrakskikh otlozheniy Dagestana. Geolog. sb., No. 1 (IV). Izd. VNIGRI.

LIVEROVSKAYA, E. V., 1953. Materials for restoration of conditions of deposition in Fergana Paleogene on molluscan evidence. Tr. VNIGRI, New Ser., no. 66. Materialy k vosstanovleniyu usloviy osadkonakopleniya v paleogene Fergany po faune mollyuskov. Tr. VNIGRI, nov. ser., vyp. 66.

LOWENSTAM, H. A., 1948. Biostratigraphic studies of the Niagaran inter-reef formations in northern Illinois. Illinois State Mus. Sci. Papers, Vol. IV.

LOWENSTAM, H. A., 1949. Niagaran reefs in Illinois and their relation to oil accumulation. Illinois State Geol. Surv. Rept. Invest., no. 145.

LOWENSTAM, H. A., 1950. Niagaran reefs of the Great Lakes area. J. Geol., 58 (4).

MAKRIDIN, V. P., 1952. Brachiopods from Upper Jurassic deposits of Donetz Range. Kharkov State Univ. Brakhiopody verkhneyurskikh otlozheniy Donetskogo kryazha. Izd. Khar'k. gos. un-ta.

MAKSIMOVA, S. V., 1949. Some peculiarities of deposition and preservation of mollusk shells. Tr. Oceanol. Inst., Vol. 4. O nekotorykh osobennostyakh zaleganiya i sokhrannosti rakovin mollyuskov. Tr. In-ta okeanologii, t. 4.

MAKSIMOVA, S. V., 1955. Facies-ecological characteristics of productive cumulation in Syzran' region. Tr. Oil Inst., Acad. Sci. U.S.S.R., Vol. 5. Fatsial'no-ekologicheskaya kharakteristika produktivnoy tolshchi Syzranskogo rayona. Tr. In-ta nefti AN SSSR, t. 5.

MAKSIMOVA, S. V. and OSIPOVA, A. I., 1950. Experience of paleoecological exploration of Upper Paleozoic terrigenous cumulations of Urals. Tr. Paleontol. Inst., Acad. Sci. U.S.S.R. Vol. 30. Opyt paleoekologicheskogo issledovaniya verkhnepaleozoyskikh terrigennykh tolshch Urala. Tr. Paleont. in-ta AN SSSR, t. 30.

MAKSIMOVA, Z. A., 1955. Trilobites of the Middle and
Upper Devonian of the Urals and northern Mugodzhar.
VSEGEI, New Ser., Vol. 3. Trilobity srednego i
verkhnego devona Urala i Severnykh Mugodzhar. Tr.
VSEGEI, nov. ser., t. 3.

MARKOVSKIY, B. P., 1954. Observations on fossil organic
remains as indications of conditions of sedimentation.
Remains of invertebrates. Methodologic textbook for
geological explorations and prospecting. VSEGEI.
Nablyudeniya nad iskopaemymi ostatkami organizmov
kak pokazatelyami usloviy otlozheniya osadochnykh
tolshch. Ostatki bespozvonochnykh. Metodicheskoe
rukovodstvo po geologicheskoy s"emke i poiskam.
VSEGEI.

MERKLIN, R. L., 1949. Paleoecological understanding of
molluscan fauna from upper tarkhan' (spiralis) days
in Kerch Peninsula. Bull. Acad. Sci. U.S.S.R., Geol.
Ser., no. 6. K poznaniyu paleoekologii mollyuskovoy
fauny verkhnetarkhanskikh (spirialisovykh) glin Kerch-
enskogo poluostrova. Izv. AN SSSR, ser. geol., No. 6.

MERKLIN, R. L., 1950. Pelecypods of spiralis days, habit
medium, and life. Tr. Paleontol. Inst., Acad. Sci.
U.S.S.R., Vol. 28. Plastinchatozhabernye spirialisovykh glin, ikh sreda i zhizn'. Tr. Paleont. in-ta AN
SSSR, t. 28.

MERKLIN, R. L., 1953. New species of oncophores in
southeastern Ustyurt. Bull. MOIP, New Ser., Vol. 58.,
Div. Geol., 25 (1). O novom vide onkofor iz yugo-
vostochnogo Ustyurta. Byull. MOIP, nov. ser., t. 58,
otd. geol., t. 25, vyp. 1.

Methodological Textbook for Geological Explorations and
Prospecting, 1954. VSEGEI, Gosgeoltekhizdat, Moscow. Metodicheskoe rukovodstvo po geologicheskoy
s"emke i poiskam. 1954. VSEGEI. Gosgeoltekhizdat.

MIKHAYLOVA, M. V., 1959. Structure and conditions of
origin of Oxford bioherms in region of Sudak Mt. Bull.
Inst. Higher Learning, Geol. Prospecting, no. 5.
Stroenie i usloviya obrazovaniya oksfordskikh bio-
germov v rayone g. Sudaka. Izv. vyssh, uchebn.
zavedeniy, geol. i razvedka, No. 5.

MILNER, H. B., 1962. Sedimentary Petrography. Mac-
Millan, New York.

MOODIE, R. L., 1923. Paleopathology. An introduction to the study of ancient evidences of disease. Univ. Illinois.

MOORE, R. C., 1957. Modern methods of Paleoecology. Bull. Am. Assoc. Petrol. Geologists, 41 (8).

MÜLLER, A. H., 1951. Grundlagen der Biostratonomie. Abhandl. deut. Akad. Wiss. Berlin, Kl. Math. allgem. Naturw., No. 7, (1950).

MÜLLER, A. H., 1957. Lehrbuch der Paläozoologie. Vol. 1, Allgemeine Grundlagen. Fischer, Jena.

NALIVKIN, B. V., 1956. Pseudoplanktonic pelecypods from Domanik. Rept. Acad. Sci. U.S.S.R., 111 (1). Pseudoplanktonnye peletsipody domanika. Dokl. AN SSSR, t. 111, No. 1.

NALIVKIN, D. V., 1956. Facies science. Geographic conditions of origin of deposits. Vols. 1 and 2. Acad. Sci. U.S.S.R. Uchenie o fatsiyakh. Geograficheskie uslov-iya obrazovaniya osadkov. T. 1 i 2. Izd. AN SSSR.

NALIVKIN, V. D., 1949. Stratigraphy and tectonics of the Ufa Plateau and Yurezan'-Sylva depression. Tr. VNIGRI, New Ser., no. 46. Stratigrafiya i tektonika Ufimskogo plato i Yurezansko-Sylvenskoy depressii. Tr. VNIGRI, nov. ser., vyp. 46.

NALIVKIN, V. D., 1950. Facies and geological history of the Ufa Plateau and Yurezan'-Sylva depression. Tr. VNIGRI, New Ser., no. 47. Fatsii i geologicheskaya istoriya Ufimskogo plato i Yurezansko-Sylvenskoy depressii. Tr. VNIGRI, nov. ser., vyp. 47.

NAUMOV, N. P., 1955. Animal ecology. Soviet Sci. Ekologiya zhivotnykh. Sov. nauka.

NEVESSKAYA, L.A., 1959. Bottom mollusk complexes of Upper Quaternary deposits in nearshore region, Black Sea (Anaysk region). Tr. Oceanog. Comm., Vol. 4. Donnye kompleksy mollyuskov verkhnechetvertichnykh otlozheniy pribrezhnoy oblasti Chernogo morya (Anay-skiy rayon). Tr. Okeanografich. komissii, t. 4.

NEWELL, N. D., RIGBY, J. K., FISCHER, A. G., WHITE-MAN, A. J., HICKOX, J. E. and BRADLEY, J. S., 1953. The Permian Reef Complex of the Guadalupe Mountains Region. Texas and New Mexico. A Study in Paleoecology. Freeman, San Francisco.

NOINSKIY, M. E., 1913. Samara Bend. Geological explorations. Tr. Soc. Naturalists, Kazan' Univ., 45 (4-6). Samarskaya Luka. Geologicheskie issledovaniya. Tr.

Obshch-va estestvoisp. pri Kazansk. un-te, t. 45, vyp. 4-6.

ORLOV, Yu. A., 1947. *Peruniinae*, new subfamily of mustelids from Eurasian Neogene. (Toward phylogeny of mustelids). Tr. Paleontol. Inst., Acad. Sci. U.S.S.R., 10 (3). *Peruniinae*, novoe podsemeystvo kunits iz neogena Evrazii. (K filogenii kunits). Tr. Paleont. in-ta AN SSSR, t. 10, vyp. 3.

ORLOV, Yu. A., 1949. Paleoneurology as one of the divisions of vertebrate paleontology. Tr. Paleontol. Inst., Acad. Sci. U.S.S.R., Vol. 20. Paleonevrologiya kak odin iz razdelov paleontologii pozvonochnykh. Tr. Paleont. in-ta AN SSSR, t. 20.

OSIPOVA, A. I., 1947. Precipitations and benthos of Lower Alai Sea in region of Isfara River (Southern Fergana). Rept. Acad. Sci. U.S.S.R., 58 (9). Osadki i bentos nizhnealayskogo morya v rayone r. Isfary (Yu. Fergana). Dokl. AN SSSR, t. 58, No. 9.

OSIPOVA, A. I., 1955. Paleoecologic-lithologic analysis of sedimentary cumulations as a basis for detailed stratigraphy. Problems of Asiatic geology, Vol. 2. Acad. Sci. U.S.S.R. Paleoekologo-litologicheskiy analiz osadochnykh tolshch kak osnova detal'noy stratigrafii. Voprosy geologii Azii, t. 2. Izd. AN SSSR.

OSIPOVA, A. I., 1956. Conditions of dolomite development in Fergana Bay of Paleogene sea. Symposium on "Types of dolomites and their genesis." Tr. Geol. Inst., Acad. Sci. U.S.S.R., no. 4. Usloviya obrazovaniya dolomitov v Ferganskom zalive paleogenovogo morya. Sb. "Tipy dolomitovykh porod i ikh genezis." Tr. Geol. in-ta AN SSSR, vyp. 4.

Paleobiologica. Vol. I (1928)—Vol. VII (1939).

PARKER, R. H., 1959. Macro-invertebrate assemblages of Central Texas coastal bays and Lagune Madre. Bull. Am. Assoc. Petrol. Geologists, 43 (9).

PETTIJOHN, F. J., 1957. Sedimentary Rocks. 2nd ed. Harper, New York.

Problems of paleobiology and biostratigraphy, 1959. Tr. 2nd Session All-Union Paleontol. Soc. Gosgeoltekhizdat. Voprosy paleobiologii i biostratigrafii. Tr. II sessii Vses. Paleontol. obshch-va. 1959. Gosgeoltekhizdat.

QUENSTEDT, W., 1927. Beiträge zum Kapitel Fossil und

Sediment vor und bei der Einbettung. Neues Jahrb.
Mineral. Geol. Paläontol., Sect. B., Vol. 58.

RAUZER-CHERNOUSOVA, D. M., 1929. On a series of
mutations of *Cardium edule*. Bull. Assoc. Sci.-Exptl.
Inst., Phys.-Math. Fac., 1st Moscow State Univ.,
2 (1). Ob odnom ryade mutatsiy *Cardium edule*. Izv.
Assots. nauchno-issled. in-tov pri fiz.-mat. fak. 1
MGU, t. 2, No. 1.

RAUZER-CHERNOUSOVA, D. M., 1950. Facies of Upper
Carboniferous and Artinskian deposits in Sterlitamak-
Ishimaevo Cis-Urals (based on fusulinid studies). Tr.
Inst. Geol. Sci., Acad. Sci. U.S.S.R., no. 119, Geol.
Ser., no. 43. Fatsii verkhnekamennougol'nykh i art-
inskikh otlozheniy Sterlitamaksko-Ishimbayskogo Pri-
ural'ya (na osnove izucheniya fuzulinid). Tr. In-ta
geol. nauk AN SSSR, vyp. 119, ser. geol., (No. 43).

RAUZER-CHERNOUSOVA, D. M. and KULIK, E.L., 1949.
On the relationship of fusulinids to facies, and on
periodicity in their development. Bull. Acad. Sci.
U.S.S.R., Ser. Geol., no. 6. Ob otnoshenii fusulinid k
fatsiyam i o periodichnosti ikh razvitiya. Izv. AN SSSR,
ser. geol., No. 6.

RAVIKOVICH, A. I., 1954. Modern and fossil reefs. Acad.
Sci. U.S.S.R. Sovremennye i iskopaemye rify. Izd. AN
SSSR.

Reports of the Committee on a Treatise on Marine Ecology
and Paleoecology, nos. 1-11, 1941-1951.

REYMENT, R. A., 1961. Controlling factors in geological
distribution of shells. Paleontol. J., no. 4. Faktory,
opredelyayushchie rasprostranenie rakovin v geolog-
icheskom proshlom. Paleont. zhurnal, No. 4.

RICHTER, R., 1919, 1920, 1923, 1925, 1926, 1934, 1937.
Von Bau und Leben der Trilobiten, I-VIII. Sencken-
bergiana Palaeontol. Hung. Zentralbl. Mineral, Geol.,
Paläontol. Zool. Anz.

RICHTER, R., 1922. Die Lage schüsselförmiger Körper
bei der Einbettung. Flachseebeobachtungen zur Paläontologie und Geologie, III. Senckenbergiana, 4 (5)
(and other numbers in this series, 1920-1926).

RICHTER, R., 1927. Die fossilen Fährten und Bauten der
Würmer, ein Überblick über ihre biologischen Grund-
formen und deren geologische Bedeutung. Päläont. Z.,
Vol. 9.

RICHTER, R., 1928a. Psychische Reaktionen fossiler Tiere. Palaeobiologica, Vol. 1.

RICHTER, R., 1928b. Aktuopaläontologie und Paläobiologie, eine Abgrenzung. Senckenbergiana, 10 (6).

RICHTER, R., 1929a. Gründung und Aufgaben der Forschungsstelle für Meeresgeologie "Senckenberg" in Wilhelmshaven. Natur und Museum, 59 (1).

RICHTER, R., 1929b. Das Verhältnis von Funktion und Form bei den Deckenkorallen. Senckenbergiana, 11 (1-2).

RICHTER, R., 1931. Tierwelt und Umwelt im Hunsrückschiefer; zur Entstehung eines schwarzen Schlammsteins. Senckenbergiana, 13 (5-6).

RICHTER, R., 1935, 1936, 1941. Marken und Spuren im Hunsrück-Schiefer, I-III. Senckenbergiana, Vols. 17, 18, 23.

RICHTER, R., 1942. Die Einkippungsregel. Senckenbergiana, 25 (7-8).

RICHTER, R., 1955. Taxiologie und Paläotaxiologie zwischen Psychologie und Physiologie. Senckenbergiana Lethaea, 36 (5-6).

RICHTER, R. and RICHTER, E., 1937, 1939, 1941. Marken und Spuren aus allen Zeiten, I-V. Senckenbergiana, Vols. 19, 21, 23.

ROGER, J., 1949. Programme d'observations et d'études marines s'appliquant à la géologie et à la paléontologie. Bull. Lab. maritime Dinard, no. 32.

RÖHLICH, P. and CHLUPÁČ, I., 1952. The Upper Ordovician in the Brickyard at Řeporyje (Central Bohemia). Sb. Ústřed. Ústavu Geol., Vol. 19, oddil. geol.

RYABININ, V. N., 1951. Stromatoporoids of the Estonian S.S.R. (Silurian and Upper Ordovician). Tr. VNIGRI, New Ser., no. 43. Stromatoporidei Estonskoy SSR. (Silur i verkhi ordovika). Tr. VNIGRI, nov. ser., vyp. 43.

SARYCHEVA, T. G., 1940. Brachiopod fauna of some shallow water deposits of Lower Carboniferous in Moscow Basin. Bull. Acad. Sci. U.S.S.R., Div. Biol. Sci. O brakhiopodovoy faune nekotorykh melkovodnykh otlozheniy nizhnego karbona Podmoskovnogo basseyna. Izv. AN SSSR, otd. biol. nauk.

SARYCHEVA, T. G., 1949a. Morphology, ecology, and evolution of Carboniferous productids in Moscow

Basin (genera *Dictyoclostus*, *Pugilis*, and *Antiqua-tonia*). Tr. Paleontol. Inst., Acad. Sci. U.S.S.R., Vol. 18. Morfologiya, ekologiya, i evolyutsiya podmoskov-nykh kamennougol'nykh produktid (rody *Dictyoclostus*, *Pugilis* i *Antiquatonia*). Tr. Paleont. in-ta AN SSSR, t. 18.

SARYCHEVA, T. G., 1949b. Damages inflicted during life-time in Carboniferous productids. Tr. Paleontol. Inst., Acad. Sci. U.S.S.R., Vol. 20. O prizhiznennykh pov-rezhdeniyakh rakovin kamennougol'nykh produktid. Tr. Paleont. in-ta AN SSSR, t. 20.

SAYANOV, V. S., 1959. Reefogenous-onkoidal construc-tions of Middle Sarmatian in Cis-Dnestr regions of Moldavian S.S.R. Bull. Moldavian Div., Acad. Sci. U.S.S.R., no. 12 (66). Rifogenno-onkoidnye obrazo-vaniya srednego sarmata pridnestrovskikh rayonov Moldavskoy SSR. Izv. Moldavsk. filiala AN SSSR, No. 12 (66).

SCHÄFER, W., 1952. Biogene Sedimentation im Gefolge von Bioturbation. Senckenbergiana, Vol. 33.

SCHÄFER, W., 1955. Fossilisations-Bedingungen der Meeressäuger und Vögel. Senckenbergiana Lethaea, 36 (1-2).

SCHÄFER, W., 1956. Wirkunger der Benthos-Organismen auf den jungen Schichtverband. Senckenbergiana Le-thaea, 37 (3-4).

SCHÄFER, W., 1962. Aktuo-Paläontologie nach Studien in der Nordsee. Senckenberg-Buch, 41. Frankfurt.

SCHINDEWOLF, O. H., 1958. Würmer und Korallen als Synöken. Zur Kenntnis der Systeme *Aspidosiphon/ Heteropsammia* und *Hicetes/ Pleurodictyum*. Abhandl. math-naturw. Kl. Akad. Wiss. Lit., no. 6.

SCHINDEWOLF, O. H. and SEILACHER, A., 1955. Beiträge zur Kenntnis des Kambriums in der Salt Range (Pakistan). Abhandl. math-naturw. Kl. Akad. Wiss. Lit., no. 10.

SCHMIDT, H., 1935. Die bionomische Einteilung der fos-silen Meeresböden. Fortschr. Geol. Paläontol., 12 (38).

SEILACHER, A., 1951. Der Röhrenbau von *Lanice con-chilega* (Polychaeta). Ein Beitrag zur Deutung fossiler Lebensspuren. Senckenbergiana, Vol. 32.

SEILACHER, A., 1953. Studien zur Palichnologie, I. Über die Methoden der Palichnologie, II. Die fossilen

Ruhespuren (Cubichnia). Neues Jahrb. Geol. Paläontol., Abhandl., 96 (3); 98 (1).

SEILACHER, A., 1954a. Die geologische Bedeutung fossiler
Lebensspuren. Z. deut. Geol. Ges., 105 (2) (1953).

SEILACHER, A., 1954b. Ökologie der triassischen Muschel
Lima lineata (Schloth.) und ihre Epöken. Neues Jahrb.
Geol. Paläontol., Monatsh., no. 4.

SEILACHER, A., 1957. Anaktualistisches Wattenmeer?
Paläontol. Z., 31 (3-4).

SEILACHER, A., 1958. Zur ökologischen Charakteristik
von Flysch und Molasse. Eclogae Geol. Helv., 51 (3).

SEILACHER, A., 1960. Epizoans as a key to ammonoid
ecology. J. Paleontol., 34 (1).

SEILACHER, A., 1962. Paleontological studies on turbidite
sedimentation and erosion. J. Geol., 70 (2).

Senckenbergiana. In editions of Senckenbergische Natur-
forschende Gesellschaft: "Senckenbergiana" (now
"Senckenbergiana Lethaea") and "Natur und Volk"
(formerly "Natur und Museum"), beginning with 1928
the works are under the general title "Senckenberg
am Meer." See Bucher, W., 1938 and Häntzschel, W.,
1956.

SHIMANSKIY, V. N., 1948. The contemporary nautilus and
its value in studying the cephalopod fossils. Sci. Ann.
Moscow State Pedagog. Inst., Vol. 52. Sovremennyy
nautilus i ego znachenie dlya izucheniya iskopaemykh
golovonogikh. Uch. Zap. Mosk. gos. ped. in-ta, t. 52.

SHVETSOV, M. S., 1932. A general geologic map of the
European U.S.S.R. Sheet 58. Northwestern quarter of
the sheet. Tr. All-Union Geol. Prospecting Soc., no.
83. Obshchaya geologicheskaya karta Evropeyskoy
chasti SSSR. List 58. Severo-Zapadnaya chetvert'
lista. Tr. Vses. geol.-razv. ob"yedin., vyp. 83.

SHVETSOV, M. S., 1938. History of the Moscow Carboniferous Basin in the Dinantian epoch. Tr. MGRI, Vol. 12.
Istoriya moskovskogo kamennougol'nogo basseyna v
dinantskuyu epokhu. Tr. MGRI, t. 12.

SHVETSOV, M. S., PUSTOVALOV, L. V. and RUKHIN, L.
B., 1957a. Methods of study of sedimentary rocks,
Vols. 1 and 2. Gosgeoltekhizdat. Metoda× izucheniya
osadochnykh porod. Gosgeoltekhizdat.

SHVETSOV, M. S., PUSTOVALOV, L. V. and RUKHIN, L.
B., 1957b. Handbook on petrography of sedimentary

rocks, Vols. 1 and 2. Gostoptekhizdat. Spravochnom rukovodstve po petrografii osadochnykh porod. Gostoptekhizdat.

SIMPSON, S., 1957. On the trace-fossil *Chondrites*. Quart. J. Geol. Soc. London, 112 (4) (1956).

SLYUSAREVA, A.D., 1960. Spiriferids of Kazanian stage in Russian Platform, and conditions of their existence. Tr. Paleontol. Inst., Acad. Sci. U.S.S.R., Vol. 80. Spiriferidy kazanskogo yarusa Russkoy platformy i usloviya ikh sushchestvovaniya. Tr. Paleont. in-ta AN SSSR, t.80.

SOBETSKIY, V. A., 1961. Upper Cretaceous *Pectinacea* in middle Dnestr Basin, their systematics and ecological peculiarities. Inst. Geol. Useful Minerals, Acad. Sci. Moldavian S.S.R. Verkhnemelovye *Pectinacea* Srednego Pridnestrov'ya, ikh sistematicheskiy sostav i ekologicheskie osobennosti. Izd. In-ta geol. i polezn. iskop. Akad. Nauk Moldavsk. SSR.

SOKOLOV, B. S., 1948. Commensalism in favositids. Bull. Acad. Sci. U.S.S.R., Biol. Ser., no. 1. Kommensalizm u favozitid. Izv. AN SSSR, ser. biol., No. 1.

SOLOV'EV, A. N., 1961. Parasite *Canceripustula nocens* in late Jurassic sea urchin. Paleontol. J., no. 4. Parazit *Canceripustula nocens* u pozdneyurskogo morskogo ezha. Paleontol. zhurnal, No. 4.

SOSHKINA, E. D., 1948. Variability of external indicators of the Devonian and Silurian *Rugosa* corals. Bull. Acad. Sci. U.S.S.R., Biol. Ser., no. 2. Izmenchivost' vneshnikh priznakov devonskikh i siluriyskikh korallov *Rugosa*. Izv. AN SSSR, ser. biol., No. 2.

STEPANOV, D. L., 1957. Dimorphism and neothery in Paleozoic brachiopods. Ann. All-Union Paleontol. Soc., Vol. 16. Dimorfizm i neoteniya u paleozoyskikh brakhiopod. Ezhegodn. Vses. Paleontol. obshch-va, t. 16.

STEPANOV, D. L., 1958. Principles and methods of biostratigraphic investigations. Tr. VNIGRI, no. 113. Printsipy i metody biostratigraficheskikh issledovaniy. Tr. VNIGRI, vyp. 113.

STRAKHOV, N. M., 1934. Combustible shales of *Perisphinctes panderi* d'Orb. zone. (Outline of lithology). Bull. MOIP, New Ser., Vol. 42, Div. Geol., 12 (2). Goryuchie slantsy zony *Perisphinctes panderi* d'Orb. (Ocherk litologii). Byull. MOIP, nov.

ser., t. 42, otd. geol., t. 12, vyp. 2.

SULTANOV, K. M., 1953. Stratigraphy and fauna of the
Upper Miocene of eastern Azerbaydzhan. Inst. Geol.,
Acad. Sci. Azerbaydzhan S.S.R. Stratigrafiya i fauna
verkhnego miotsena Vostochnogo Azerbaydzhana. In-ta
geol. AN Azerbaydzh. SSR.

TARASOV, N. I., 1951. The living sea. 3rd ed. Soviet Sci.
More zhivet. 3-e izd. Sov. nauka.

TAUBER, A. F., 1942. Postmortale Veränderungen an
Molluskenschalen und ihre Auswertbarkeit für die
Erforschung vorzeitlicher Lebensräume. Palaeobio-
logica, Vol. 7.

TERMIER, H. and TERMIER, G., 1952. Histoire géologique
de la biosphère. (La vie et les sédiments dans les
géographies successives). Paris.

Treatise on Marine Ecology and Paleoecology, 1957. Vol.
1, Ecology. Vol. 2, Paleocology. Geol. Soc. Am.
Mem., no. 67.

TRIZNA, V. B., 1950. Characteristics of the reef and layer
facies of the central part of the Ufa Plateau. Microfauna of oil deposits of the U.S.S.R., Collection 3. Tr.
VNIGRI, New Ser., no. 50. K kharakteristike rifovykh
i sloistykh fatsiy tsentral'noy chasti Ufimskogo plato.
Mikrofauna neftyanykh mestorozhdeniy SSSR, sb. III.
Tr. VNIGRI, nov. ser., vyp. 50.

VAN STRAATEN, L. M. J. U., 1964. Deltaic and Shallow
Marine Deposits.

VARSANOF'YEVA, V.A. and GEKKER, R. F., 1951. Preservation of natural landmarks. All-Russian Conserva-
tion Soc. Press. Okhrana pamyatnikov nezhivoy prirody. Izd. Vseross. obshch-va okhr. prirody.

VASSOEVICH, N. B., 1932. Some indicators which permit
the differentiation of the reversed position of flysch
formations from normal formations. Tr. Geol. Inst.,
Acad. Sci. U.S.S.R., Vol. 2. O nekotorykh priznakakh,
pozvolyayushchikh otlichit' oprokinutoe polozhenie
flishevykh obrazovaniy ot normal'nogo. Tr. Geol. in-ta
AN SSSR, t. 2.

VASSOEVICH, N. B., 1948. Flysch and methods of studying
it. VNIGRI. Flish i metodika ego izucheniya. Izd.
VNIGRI.

VASSOEVICH, N. B., 1951. Flysch formation conditions.
VNIGRI. Usloviya obrazovaniya flisha. Izd. VNIGRI.

VASSOEVICH, N. B., 1953. Some flysch textures. Tr.
L'vov Geol. Soc., Ser. Geol., no. 3. O nekotorykh
flishevykh teksturakh. Tr. L'vovsk. geol. obshch-va,
ser. geol., vyp. 3.

VOIGT, E., 1956. Der Nachweis des Phytals durch Epizoen
als Kriterium der Tiefe vorzeitlicher Meere. Geol.
Rundschau, 45 (1).

VOROB'EV, V. P., 1949. Benthos of the Sea of Azov. Tr.
Azov-Black Sea Sci. Res. Inst. Marine Fisheries and
Oceanog., no. 13. Bentos Azovskogo morya. Tr.
Azovsko-Chernomorsk. nauchno-issled. in-ta morsk.
rybn. khoz. i okeanografii, vyp. 13.

VOYNOVSKIY-KRIGER, K., 1945. Significance of problem-
atic fossilizations and the necessity for their collection and study. Yearbook Russian Paleontol. Soc., Vol.
12, 1936-1939. O znachenii problematicheskikh oka-
menelostey i o neobkhodimosti ikh sbora i izucheniya.
Ezhegodnik Russkogo paleont. obshch-va, t. 12, 1936-
1939.

VYALOV, O. S. and FLEROV, K. K., 1952. Fossil remains
of vertebrates in the Tertiary deposits of Cis-Car-
pathia. Bull. MOIP, New Ser., Vol. 57, Div. Geol.,
27 (5). Iskopaemye sledy pozvonochnykh v tretichnykh
otlozheniyakh Predkarpat'ya. Byull. MOIP, nov. ser.,
t. 57, otd. geol., t. 27, vyp. 5.

WALTHER, J., 1893-1894. Einleitung in die Geologie als
historische Wissenschaft. Vols. I-III. Fischer, Jena.

WALTHER, J., 1904. Die Fauna der Solnhofener Platten-
kalke, bionomisch betrachtet (Festschrift für E.
Haechel). Fischer, Jena.

WALTHER, J., 1919-1927. Allgemeine Paläontologie. Geologische Probleme in biologischer Betrachtung. Parts
I-IV. Berlin.

WASMUND, E., 1926. Biocoenose und Thanatocoenose.
Biosoziologische Studie der Lebensgemeinschaften
und Totengesellschaften. Arch. Hydrobiol., Vol. 17.

WEIGELT, J., 1923. Angewandte Geologie und Paläontologie
der Flachseegesteine und das Erzlager von Salzgitter.
Fortschr. Geol. Paläontol., no. 4.

WEIGELT, J., 1927a. Über Biostratonomie. Der Geologe,
no. 42.

WEIGELT, J., 1927b. Rezente Wirbeltierleichen und ihre
paläobiologische Bedeutung. Der Geologe.

YAKOVLEV, N. N., 1907. The increase of shells of several *Strophomenacea* (*Meekella, Strophalosia, Aulosteges*). Bull. Geol. Comm., 26 (4). O prirostanii rakoviny nekotorykh *Strophomenacea* (*Meekella, Strophalosia, Aulosteges*). Izv. Geol. kom., t. 26, No. 4.

YAKOVLEV, N. N., 1908. Sedentary brachiopods as the basis for types and genera. Tr. Geol. Comm., New Ser., no. 48. Prikleplenie brakhiopod kak osnova vidov i rodov. Tr. Geol. kom., nov. ser., vyp. 48.

YAKOVLEV, N. N., 1910. The origin of distinctive features of *Rugosa*. Tr. Geol. Comm., New Ser., no. 66. O proiskhozhdenii kharakternykh osobennostey *Rugosa*. Tr. Geol. kom., nov. ser., vyp. 66.

YAKOVLEV, N. N., 1911. Did coral reefs exist in the Paleozoic? Bull. Geol. Comm., Vol. 30. Sushchestvuyut li korallovye rify v paleozoe? Izv. Geol. kom., t. 30.

YAKOVLEV, N. N., 1914. Studies of *Rugosa* corals. Tr. Geol. Comm., New Ser., no. 96. Etyudy o korallakh *Rugosa*. Tr. Geol. kom., nov. ser., vyp. 96.

YAKOVLEV, N. N., 1926. The phenomena of parasitism, commensalism, and symbiosis in invertebrates of the Paleozoic. Yearbook Russian Paleontol. Soc., Vol. 4 (1922-1924). Yavleniya parazitizma, kommensalizma i simbioza u paleozoyskikh bespozvonochnykh. Ezhegodnik Russk. paleont. obshch-va, t. 4 (1922-1924).

YAKOVLEV, N. N., 1927. Ancient wood-boring gastropods. Yearbook Russian Paleontol. Soc., Vol. 6 (1926). O drevneyshikh sverlyashchikh gastropodakh. Ezhegodnik Russk. paleont. obshch-va, t. 6 (1926).

YAKOVLEV, N. N., 1945. The morphology of *Rugosa* corals. Bull. Acad. Sci. U.S.S.R., Div. Biol. Sci., no. 3. Morfologiya korallov *Rugosa*. Izv. AN SSSR, otd. biol. nauk, No. 3.

YAKOVLEV, N. N., 1952. Organisms and media. J. Gen. Biol., 13 (2), Acad. Sci. U.S.S.R. Organizm i sreda. Zhurn. obshch. biol., t. 13, No. 2. Izd. AN SSSR.

YAKOVLEV, N. N., 1956. Organisms and media. Works on the paleoecology of invertebrates, 1913-1956. Div. Biol. Sci., Acad. Sci. U.S.S.R. Organizm i sreda. Stat'i po paleoekologii bespozvonochnykh 1913-1956 gg. Izd. biol. nauk AN SSSR.

ZENKEVICH, L. A., 1947, 1951. The fauna and biological productivity of the sea. Vol. 1, 1951; Vol. 2, 1947.

Soviet Sci. Fauna i biologicheskaya produktivnost' morya. T. I, 1951; t. II, 1947. Sov. nauka.

ZENKEVICH, L. A., 1956. Seas of the U.S.S.R., their fauna and flora. 2nd ed. Uchpedgiz. Morya SSSR, ikh fauna i flora. 2-e izd. Uchpedgiz.

ZERNOV, S. A., 1913. Study of life in the Black Sea. Rept. Acad. Sci., 8th Ser., 32 (1). K voprosu ob izuchenii zhizni Chernogo morya. Zap. Akad. nauk, VIII ser., t. 32, No. 1.

ZERNOV, S. A., 1949. General hydrobiology. 2nd ed. Acad. Sci. U.S.S.R. Obshchaya gidrobiologiya. 2-e izd. Izd. AN SSSR.

ZHURAVLEVA, I. T. and ZELENOV, K. K., 1955. Bioherms of the varicolored formation of the Lena River. Collection of mateiral on the fauna and flora of the Paleozoic of Siberia. Tr. Paleontol. Inst., Acad. Sci. U.S.S.R., Vol. 56. Biogermy pestrotsvetnoy svity reki Leny. Sb. Materialy po faune i flore paleozoya Sibiri. Tr. Paleont. in-ta AN SSSR, t. 56.

Index

Oil, 18, 35
Ontongeny, 6
Ophiuroids, 17, 19
Ordovician bryozoan, 40
Ordovician deposits, 26
Ordovician of North America, 46
Oryctocoenosis, 20
Ostracodes, 17, 44
Oxygen, 20, 21
Oyster shells, 40
Oysters, 54

Palaeosabella, 40
Paleobiocoenoses, 11, 58
Paleocoenosis, 16n
Paleoclimatology, 26
Paleoecological-lithological analysis, 15
Paleoecological maps, 81, 82
Paleoecological monuments, 94
Paleoecologic profiles, 71
Paleogene deposits, 8, 32
Paleogene Sea, 8, 55, 94
Paleogeography, 26, 61
Paleontological Institute of Academy of Sciences of U.S.S.R., 84
Paleopathology, 43
Paleosynecological monograph, 57
Paleothanatocoenosis, 17
Paleozoic favositids, 40
Parallelism, 93
Parasites, 20, 40
Parasitism, 39, 40
Pathological phenomena, 43
Pelecypod forms, 17
Pelecypods, 18, 40, 54, 56
Pelecypod shell, 5
Pelecypod valves, 35, 39
Permian Age, 46
Permian fishes, 2
Permian reefs, 46
Petrographic specimens, 51
Petroleum, 46
Pettijohn, F. J., 37n
Phyletic lineages, 6
Phyletic stage, 5n
Phyletic tree, 79, 80
Phylogenetic development, 59
Phylogenetic lineages, 26
Phylogenetic trees, 26
Phylogeny, 79
Phytogeography, 11
Planktonic organisms, 74
Planktonic tentaculities, 37
Platforms, 23
Platyceras, 44

Pleurodictyum problematicum Goldf., 40
Polydora, 40
Predatory mammals, 43
Predatory mollusks, 43
Problematica, 41, 42
Pteropods, 17
Pustovalov, L. V., 37n

Quaternary deposits, 2
Quaternary mollusks, 42
Quenstedt, W., 20

Reefs, 46
Rhizocorallium, 42
Rhizolites, 42
Richter, 43
Richter, R., 9, 10
Rock-boring mollusks, 94
"Rock-living" oysters, 94
Rock matrix, 50, 51
Rouillier, K. F., 2
Rugosa corals, 39
Rukhin, L. B., 37n
Russia, 1
Russian Platform, 11, 26, 27, 39

Salinity, 4, 5, 12, 13, 23, 32, 33, 77, 78
Sataplia hill, 94
Scaphoideus Zhizh., 18
Schematic sketches, 62
Schvetsov, M. S., 36n
"Seal of environment," 11, 18
Sea urchins, 55
"Second Baku," 46
Sedimentary facies, 76
Sedimentary petrologist, 22, 36
Sedimentary profile, 71
Sedimentological maps, 81, 82
Sediments, 8
Serpula, 43
Sevastopol, 10
Shell distortion, 6
Shelon' horizon, 32
Silurian of British Baltic, 46
Silurian of North America, 46
Solnhofen, 45
Solnhofen shales, 15
Spirophyton, 42
Sponges, 46
Starfishes, 19
Stenobiontic, 12
Stenohaline, 71